Disney **LEARNING**

GRADE

3

NELSON

This workbook belongs to:

_____

Disney LEARNING

Published by Nelson Education Ltd.

ISBN-13: 978-0-17-685502-4
ISBN-10: 0-17-685502-5

Printed and bound in Canada
1 2 3 4   21 20 19 18

For more information contact Nelson Education Ltd.,
1120 Birchmount Road, Toronto, Ontario M1K 5G4.
Or you can visit our website at nelson.com.

For permission to use material from this text or product,
submit all requests online at cengage.com/permissions.
Further questions about permissions can be emailed to
permissionrequest@cengage.com.

Credits: 23, 48, 49, 113, 114: Coin images © 2018 Royal Canadian Mint. Bank note image used with the permission of the Bank of Canada.

Contents

Track Your Learning

START

1 2 3 4

24 23 22 21 20 19 18 17

25 26 27 28 29 30

51 50 49 48 47 46 45

52 53 54 55 56 57 58 59

79 78 77 76 75 74 73

80 81 82 83 84 85 86

Colour a circle for every completed activity to finish the Brain Boost learning path!

5   6   7   8   9   10

16   15   14   13   12   11

31   32   33   34   35   36   37   38

44   43   42   41   40   39

60   61   62   63   64   65   66   67

72   71   70   69   68

87   88   89   90   **FINISH**

Function Box

Hiro is designing a new robot.

Solve each equation to check Hiro's calculations.

4 → + 0 = →

→ − 0 = → 13

20 → + 0 = →

→ − 0 = → 45

100 → + 0 = →

→ − 0 = → 99

598 → + 0 = →

→ − 0 = → 780

1000 → − 0 = →

What do you notice when you add or subtract 0? _____

_____

Fill In the Blanks

The microbots are sucked backward into the portal. Yokai slowly has fewer and fewer microbots under his control.

Count backward by 10s from 50 to 0.
Fill in each missing number.

50, _____, _____, _____, _____, 0

Count backward by 10s from 95 to 25.
Fill in each missing number.

95, _____, _____, _____, _____, _____, _____, 25

Count backward by 5s from 70 to 40. Fill in each missing number.

70, _____, _____, _____, _____, _____, 40

Count backward by 5s from 35 to 0. Fill in each missing number.

35, _____, _____, _____, _____, _____, _____, 0

Count backward by 2s from 54 to 38. Fill in each missing number.

54, _____, _____, _____, _____, _____, _____, _____, 38

Count backward by 2s from 90 to 76. Fill in each missing number.

90, _____, _____, _____, _____, _____, _____, 76

HINT Look for the pattern in the ones digits as you count backward by 2s, 5s, or 10s.

Crack the Code

Hiro and Baymax can't get out of the portal.

Count backward in each pattern. Fill in each missing number. Then use the letter that matches each number to crack the code. The first one is done for you.

100, 90, __**80**__, 70, 60, 50, 40, _____
            R   T

75, 70, _____, 60, 55, 50, _____, 40
          S   C

20, 18, _____, 14, 12, 10, 8, 6, _____
          T   O

40, 35, 30, _____, 20, 15, _____, 5
            K   I

60, 50, _____, 30, 20, 10, _____
          H

_____, 56, 54, _____, 50, 48, _____, 44
  I   S   E

What does Baymax use to save Hiro?

____ ____ ____   **R** ____ ____ ____ ____ ____
40   58   65   80   4   45   25   46   30

____ ____ ____ ____
0   10   52   16

HINT Determine the pattern first to decide by how much to count backward.

Matching

Baymax is so cuddly. Mochi loves attention. Together they make a good match!

Match each 3-digit number with the correct number word.

343   two hundred thirty-nine

506   three hundred eighty-seven

985   five hundred six

101   one hundred one

239   nine hundred eighty-five

880   three hundred forty-three

748   seven hundred forty-eight

672   four hundred fifty-four

454   eight hundred eighty

387   six hundred seventy two

HINT Say the number. Look for the words that match it.

Word Search

Bing Bong leads Joy and Sadness through hundreds of memories to Imagination Land.

All of these numbers are in the hundreds. Write each number. Then (circle) it in the number search. The first one is done for you.

seven hundred sixty-three ___763___

two hundred ninety-seven _____

four hundred eighty-one _____

one hundred fifty-four _____

five hundred seventy-six _____

eight hundred twenty-one _____

nine hundred twelve _____

three hundred one _____

1	8	7	6	3	0	3
2	2	3	4	1	5	0
9	1	2	7	1	3	1
0	9	2	4	6	0	9
8	2	0	2	4	8	1
2	9	4	6	8	5	5
5	7	6	0	8	7	4

HINT The numbers appear both across and down.

8

Maze

Joy and Sadness have to find their way back to Headquarters.

Find your way through the maze. Follow the numbers from least to greatest.

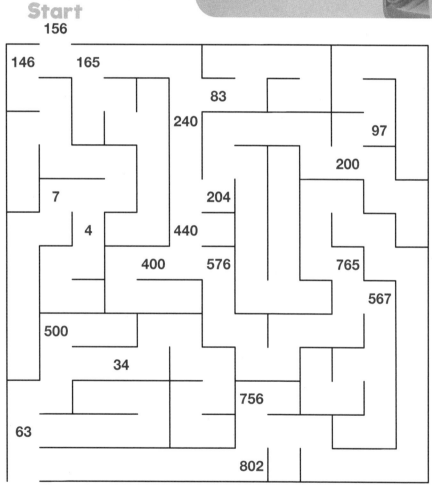

Start
156

146   165

83

240

97

200

7

204

4   440

400   576   765

567

500

34

756

63

802

Finish

HINT The smallest number will have the fewest hundreds.
The greatest number will have the most hundreds.

Colour to Complete

From tallest to shortest, the Emotions are Joy, Fear, Sadness, Disgust, and Anger.

Colour to order each set of numbers from greatest to least. Use yellow for the greatest number, followed by purple, blue, green, and red.

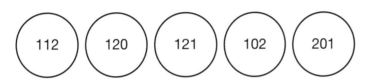

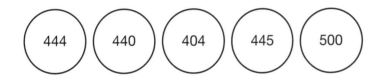

HINT Compare the hundreds digits first, then the tens, and then the ones to determine the order of the numbers.

Fill In the Blanks

Anger is really angry. Sometimes he has greater control over Riley than the other Emotions do.

For each pair of numbers, write the number that is greater.

240   204   _____

567   576   _____

709   790   _____

110   101   _____

343   344   _____

668   686   _____

For each pair of numbers, write the number that is lesser.

106   160   _____

602   603   _____

421   412   _____

863   873   _____

907   909   _____

458   358   _____

Crack the Code

When Anger is really upset, he yells. His mouth is open wide, just like the greater than and less than symbols.

Use the key to fill in each missing number. Then show which three-digit number is greater and which is lesser by writing < or > in the box. The first one is done for you.

Number Code

1	2	3	4	5	6	7	8	9	0
★	🐚	✿	♥	♫	🌴	🚲	❄	⛵	☺

8__12
❄

<

9__14
⛵

____76
🌴

51____
♫

93_____
❄

____86
🐚

1_____0
✿

43_____
♥

79_____
🚲

_____ _____4
★   ✿

_____ _____9
🚲   🐚

78_____
🐚

HINT Think of < and > as the mouth of a hungry alligator. The mouth always opens to eat the greater number.

Picture Clues

Fear sees 20 memories on the Memory Shelves.

Estimate the number of memories below. _____

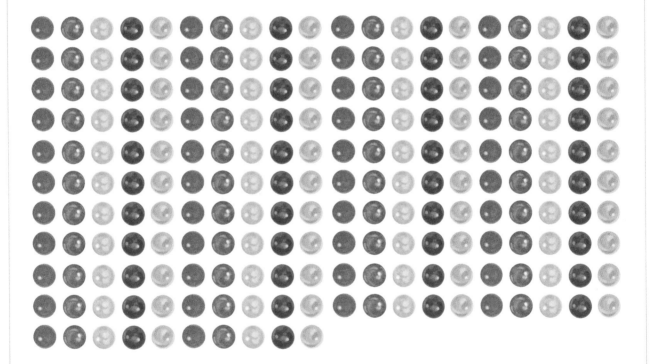

Check your estimate. _____

HINT Use the group of 20 memories at the top to help you estimate the larger group of memories.

Graphing

Go Go likes to chew gum while she works on her maglev bicycle.

Use this graph to estimate how many pieces of each flavour gum she has.

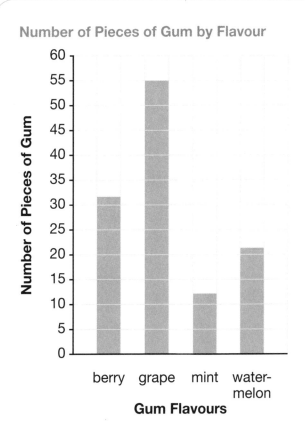

berry: about _____ pieces

grape: about _____ pieces

mint: about _____ pieces

watermelon: about _____ pieces

HINT When the number in the ones place is five or more, round up.
When it is four or less, round down.

Colour to Complete

Tadashi takes Hiro to the university to convince him to stop wasting his time on bot fights.

What are the school's initials? To find out, colour the picture. Use the Colour Key.

Colour Key

rounding to 10 rounding to 20 rounding to 30

rounding to 40 rounding to 50

49	54	45		52
8	21	27	51	42
54	5	51	53		48	36
7	52	15	51	49	34	46		
51	18		52	44	46	47
9	45					
5	54	33	25		
53	47	53		

15

Matching

The Big Hero 6 realize that if they want to defeat Yokai, they have to divide up his microbots. Each hero takes on a sixth of the microbots.

Match each fraction with the correct picture.

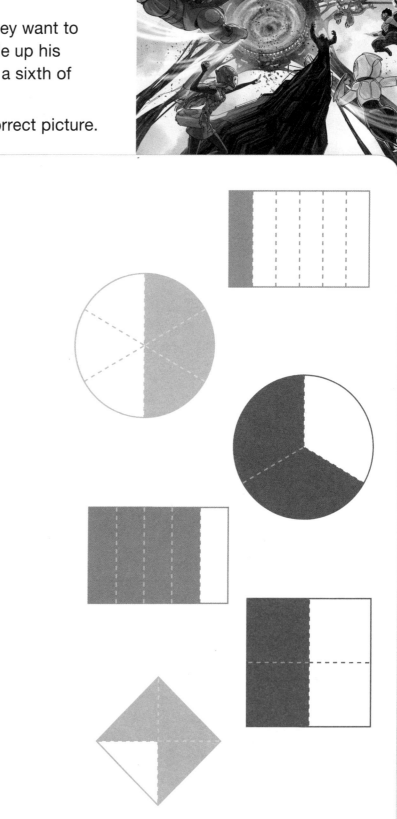

three fourths

two fourths

four fifths

one sixth

two thirds

three sixths

HINT The first word tells you how many sections are shaded. The second word is the fractional name. It tells you how many sections there are in total.

Colour to Complete

Wasabi lays out his tools so he can clearly see each one. One third of Wasabi's wrenches are blue.

Show each fraction. Colour the correct number of wrenches.

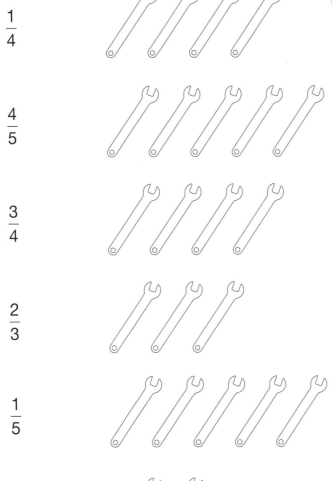

$\frac{1}{4}$

$\frac{4}{5}$

$\frac{3}{4}$

$\frac{2}{3}$

$\frac{1}{5}$

$\frac{1}{2}$

Colour to Complete

Riley is drawing a picture of her trip to Australia. She starts by dividing a piece of paper into thirds for the sky, water, and land.

Divide and colour the squares to show each fraction.

one half

six eighths

three fourths

two halves

one fourth

three eighths

HINT When you divide the squares, make sure the pieces are the same size.

Picture Clues

Riley's Emotions have some features in common. Other features are different.

Use fractions to describe the Emotions. Write the fractions out in words or numbers.

What fraction of the Emotions have blue eyes? _____

_____

What fraction of the Emotions are wearing glasses? _____

_____

What fraction of the Emotions are holding a memory? _____

_____

What fraction of the Emotions are wearing a dress? _____

_____

What fraction of the Emotions have green hair? _____

_____

What fraction of the Emotions are wearing a hat? _____

_____

Colour to Complete

It is pizza night! Riley wants to make sure there is no broccoli on her slices of pizza.

Divide each pizza. Then draw the toppings.

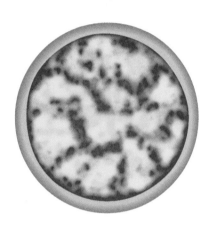

Draw broccoli on one half of the pizza.

Draw peppers on one fourth of the pizza.

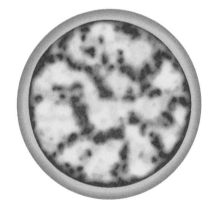

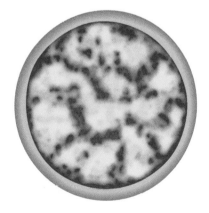

Draw mushrooms on one eighth of the pizza.

Draw pepperoni on four fourths of the pizza.

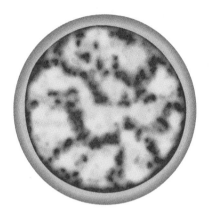

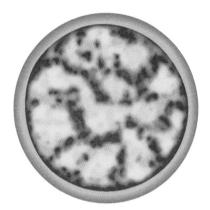

Draw olives on two fourths of the pizza.

Draw pineapple on three fourths of the pizza.

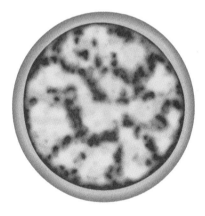

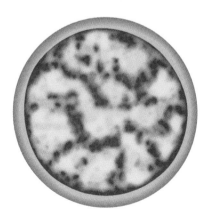

Draw ham on two eighths of the pizza.

HINT Make sure that when you divide the pizza, all the slices are the same size.

Colour to Complete

The flower Bing Bong wears has six petals.
One sixth of the petals is red.

Show each fraction by colouring in the petals.
The first one is done for you.

one third

one half

five sixths

four fourths

three fifths

two thirds

seven sevenths

six eighths

Word Search

Riley looks in her mom's wallet. In it, she sees different coins.

Write the value of each coin. Write the name of each coin. Find the name of each coin in the word search.

 value: _____ name: _____

 value: _____ name: _____

 value: _____ name: _____

 value: _____ name: _____

value: _____ name: _____

D	Q	D	E	A	D	D	T	G	J
B	U	V	L	N	I	C	K	E	L
C	J	K	J	G	M	I	P	Z	Z
X	V	P	G	B	E	K	L	U	Q
F	D	L	W	A	B	W	C	L	W
Q	U	A	R	T	E	R	T	O	Y
S	F	F	N	A	Z	B	R	O	D
P	M	L	W	Q	U	V	Z	N	L
W	F	E	J	S	N	P	R	I	N
F	P	A	T	O	O	N	I	E	Q

HINT Use a dictionary to check your spelling of each word.

Graphing

Hiro loves to go to bot fights! He loves winning them even more.

This bar graph shows how many bot fights Hiro might win in one week. Use the graph to answer each question.

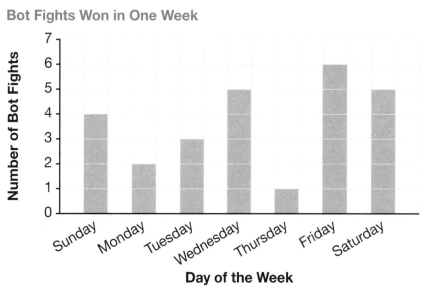

Bot Fights Won in One Week

How many fights altogether does Hiro win on Monday and Tuesday?

_____

How many fights altogether does Hiro win on Saturday and Sunday?

_____

On how many days does Hiro win four fights or more?

_____

How many more fights does Hiro win on Friday than on Thursday?

_____

Fill In the Blanks

Hiro sees hundreds of microbots falling off a conveyor belt into a barrel. Somebody has stolen his design!

Use this number line. Practise counting forward by 25s.

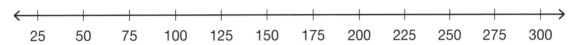

25   50   75   100   125   150   175   200   225   250   275   300

If the machine makes 25 microbots every minute, how many microbots are made in 5 minutes? _____

_____

How many microbots are made in 10 minutes? _____

_____

Start at 500 and count forward by 25s to 775. Write the numbers you counted.

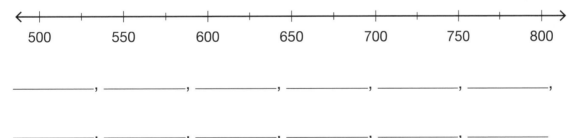

500   550   600   650   700   750   800

_____ , _____ , _____ , _____ , _____ , _____ ,

_____ , _____ , _____ , _____ , _____ , _____

Start at 725 and count forward by 25s to 1000. Write the numbers you counted.

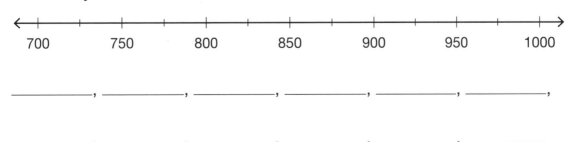

700   750   800   850   900   950   1000

_____ , _____ , _____ , _____ , _____ , _____ ,

_____ , _____ , _____ , _____ , _____ , _____

Colour to Complete

Fred has a collection of beanies. He has so many, he's lost count. He may have hundreds of beanies!

Base ten blocks can be used to represent numbers.
318 is represented by 3 flats, 1 rod, and 8 units.

Colour in the base ten blocks to represent each number.

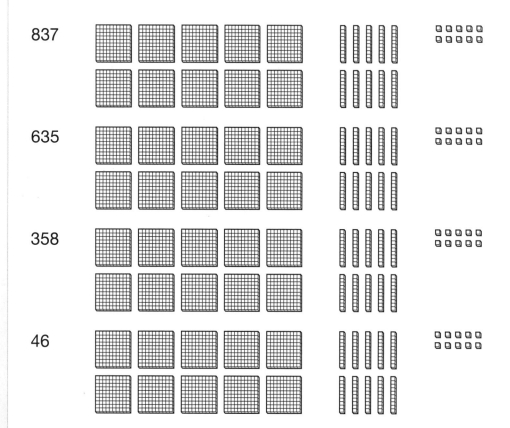

837

635

358

46

HINT A flat represents 100 ones. A rod represents 10 ones.
A unit represents one.

Picture Clues

Go Go's armour is composed of hundreds of different parts.

Complete the table. The first row is done for you.

Number	Hundreds	Tens	Ones
456	□ □ □ □	‖‖‖	◦ ◦ ◦ ◦ ◦ ◦
_____	▦ ▦	▮	◦ ◦ ◦
91			
_____	▦ ▦ ▦ ▦ ▦ ▦	‖‖‖‖‖	◦ ◦ ◦ ◦ ◦ ◦ ◦ ◦
544			
_____	▦ ▦ ▦ ▦ ▦ ▦ ▦	‖‖	◦ ◦ ◦ ◦

Fill In the Blanks

Each street in San Fransokyo has many buildings.
When you add them up, there are hundreds of
houses, offices, and apartment buildings.

Fill in the blanks to complete each addition sentence.

300 + _____ + 5 = 365

_____ + 30 + 7 = 337

_____ + 3 = 83

400 + 80 + _____ = 483

_____ + 90 + 9 = 599

800 + 60 + _____ = 860

100 + _____ + 9 = 119

_____ + 20 + 6 = 126

700 + 50 + _____ = 752

300 + _____ + 9 = 389

600 + _____ + 3 = 643

500 + _____ + 8 = 508

_____ + 80 + 9 = 989

200 + 30 + _____ = 234

HINT Think of hundreds, tens, and ones to determine each missing number.

Puzzle Pieces

Hiro and Baymax have found Yokai's warehouse. Yokai orders thousands of microbots to attack them!

Draw a line between the two puzzle pieces that make the smallest 4-digit number possible. Now, draw a line between the two puzzle pieces that make the largest 4-digit number.

91

23

82

37

smallest 4-digit number: _____

largest 4- digit number: _____

Write two other 4-digit numbers you can make with the puzzle pieces.

_____ _____

Write the four numbers you made in order from greatest to least.

_____ , _____ , _____ , _____

HINT To find the smallest and largest numbers, use the place value chart on page 112.

Function Box

When Joy tries to get rid of a sad memory, the vacuum tube sucks her and Sadness right out of Headquarters and into Mind World.

Numbers have also been sucked into a vacuum tube! Determine the missing numbers for each addition sentence.

20	+ 15 =			48	+ 78 =	
	+ 12 =	34		58	+ =	89
16	+ =	32		35	+ 18 =	
22	+ 17 =			37	+ =	72
	+ 13 =	31			+ 76 =	88
36	+ 11 =			44	+ =	75
19	+ =	40		20	+ 79 =	
	+ 18 =	61			+ 17 =	53

HINT You can use the 100-chart on page 111 to help you.

Crack the Code

Sadness can sometimes help others feel better.

Calculate each sum. Then use the letter that matches each sum to crack the code.

Letter Code

15 + 50 = _____ **A**   31 + 11 = _____ **J**   19 + 30 = _____ **S**

24 + 14 = _____ **B**   31 + 5 = _____ **K**   28 + 22 = _____ **T**

43 + 31 = _____ **C**   44 + 12 = _____ **L**   29 + 28 = _____ **U**

16 + 16 = _____ **D**   29 + 10 = _____ **M**   18 + 27 = _____ **V**

37 + 21 = _____ **E**   23 + 18 = _____ **N**   17 + 9 = _____ **W**

28 + 39 = _____ **F**   30 + 24 = _____ **O**   14 + 16 = _____ **X**

25 + 18 = _____ **G**   44 + 39 = _____ **P**   6 + 13 = _____ **Y**

29 + 24 = _____ **H**   17 + 60 = _____ **Q**   12 + 21 = _____ **Z**

14 + 26 = _____ **I**   35 + 33 = _____ **R**

What does Sadness do to help Bing Bong feel better?

She _____ _____ _____ _____ _____ _____ _____.
   56   40   49   50   58   41   49

HINT **Sum** is another word for the answer to an addition problem.

Function Box

When Joy and Sadness leave Headquarters, the remaining Emotions argue over the control panel.

Determine the missing numbers for each subtraction sentence.

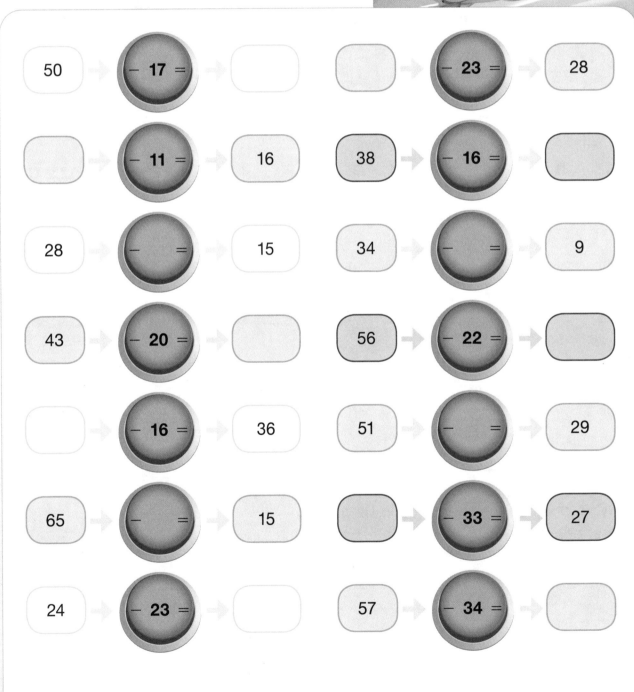

50	− 17 =			− 23 =	28
	− 11 =	16	38	− 16 =	
28	− =	15	34	− =	9
43	− 20 =		56	− 22 =	
	− 16 =	36	51	− =	29
65	− =	15		− 33 =	27
24	− 23 =		57	− 34 =	

Crack the Code

Riley went on adventures with Bing Bong when she was younger.

Determine each difference. Then use the letter that matches each difference to crack the code.

Letter Code

88 − 44 = _____ **A**   42 − 11 = _____ **J**   56 − 30 = _____ **S**

52 − 13 = _____ **B**   76 − 65 = _____ **K**   39 − 29 = _____ **T**

99 − 54 = _____ **C**   48 − 13 = _____ **L**   22 − 19 = _____ **U**

43 − 16 = _____ **D**   40 − 20 = _____ **M**   31 − 18 = _____ **V**

61 − 29 = _____ **E**   68 − 38 = _____ **N**   16 − 7 = _____ **W**

28 − 20 = _____ **F**   38 − 16 = _____ **O**   58 − 21 = _____ **X**

24 − 18 = _____ **G**   83 − 33 = _____ **P**   93 − 32 = _____ **Y**

82 − 24 = _____ **H**   60 − 35 = _____ **Q**   85 − 23 = _____ **Z**

37 − 16 = _____ **I**   47 − 23 = _____ **R**

How did Riley and Bing Bong travel?

On a ____ ____ ____ ____ ____ ____
      24   22   45   11   32   10

____ ____ ____ ____ ____ .
 9   44   6   22   30

HINT **Difference** is another word for the solution to a subtraction problem.

33

Maze

Joy and Sadness are lost. They need to figure out the shortest way to get back to Headquarters.

Which path has numbers that add up to a smaller sum? Draw a star on the path with the smaller sum.

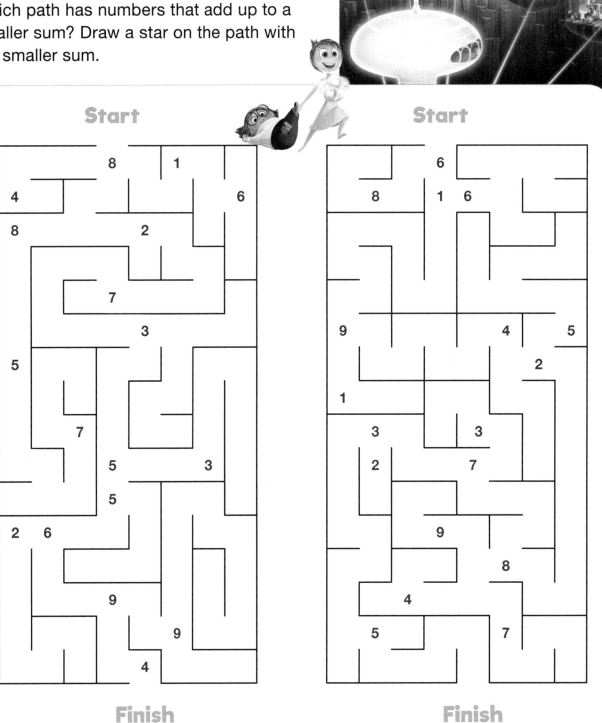

Colour to Complete

The Emotions are reviewing Riley's memories.

Colour three circles so that the numbers in them add up to the number of memories each Emotion finds. Use yellow for Joy, blue for Sadness, purple for Fear, green for Disgust, and red for Anger. The first one is done for you.

Joy finds 34 yellow memories.

Sadness finds 28 blue memories.

Fear finds 25 purple memories.

Disgust finds 20 green memories.

Anger finds 17 red memories.

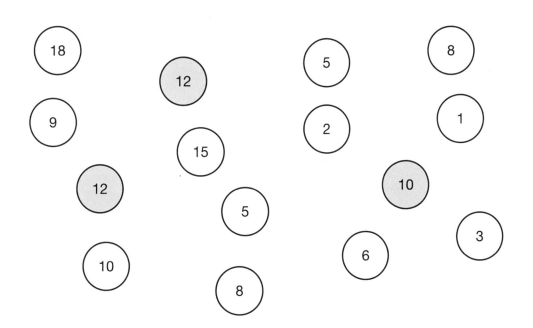

HINT First find pairs of numbers that add to 10. Then add on.

Crack the Code

Hiro and Baymax return to the warehouse to face the masked man. Baymax uses his new martial arts moves!

Determine each difference. Then use the letters matched to each difference to crack the code.

Letter Code

60 − 34 = _____ A   74 − 13 = _____ J   58 − 39 = _____ S

79 − 23 = _____ B   96 − 48 = _____ K   34 − 27 = _____ T

92 − 45 = _____ C   21 − 8 = _____ L   21 − 7 = _____ U

25 − 14 = _____ D   50 − 30 = _____ M   67 − 25 = _____ V

38 − 32 = _____ E   23 − 18 = _____ N   16 − 7 = _____ W

86 − 74 = _____ F   87 − 16 = _____ O   83 − 28 = _____ X

52 − 14 = _____ G   63 − 33 = _____ P   46 − 31 = _____ Y

45 − 23 = _____ H   77 − 56 = _____ Q   25 − 23 = _____ Z

63 − 31 = _____ I   91 − 22 = _____ R

What does Baymax do?

___ ___ ___ ___ ___   ___ ___
48   32   47   48   19   32   5

___ ___ ___   ___ ___ ___ ___.
7   22   6   11   71   71   69

HINT You can use the 100-chart on page 111 to help you.

Maze

Baymax is determined to take the microbot to where it wants to go.

Which path has numbers that subtract to 0? Draw a star on the path that has a final difference of 0.

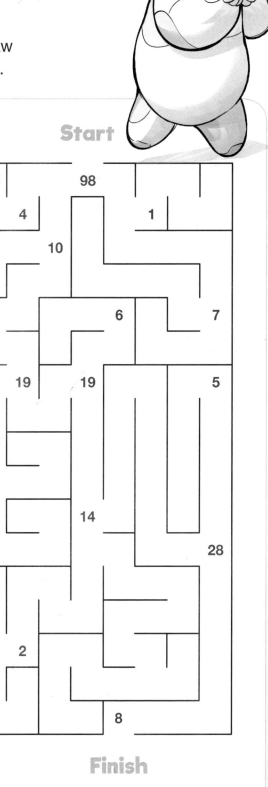

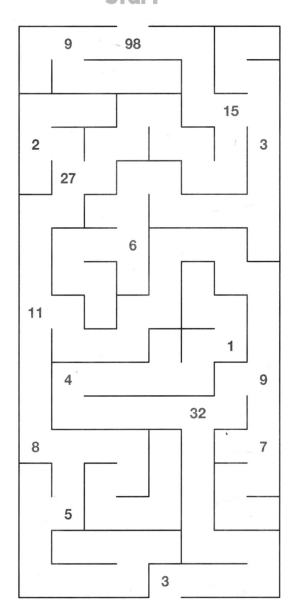

HINT Solve each maze first. Subtract the numbers on each path through the maze.

Picture Clues

Joy and Sadness have to find Riley's core memories and bring them back to Headquarters. They have to search through many memories to find them.

Estimate how many memories are in each group. _____

_____

Estimate how many memories there are altogether. _____

_____

Estimate how many memories are in each group. _____

_____

Estimate how many memories there are altogether. _____

_____

Matching

Riley plays on the Fog Horns hockey team.

Last year the Fog Horns scored 38 goals. This year they scored 53 goals. Altogether they scored about 90 goals.

Match each addition statement to the best estimate. Round each number first. Then add to estimate the sum.

38 + 53	about 20
36 + 26	about 30
8 + 47	about 40
12 + 33	about 50
9 + 13	about 60
62 + 35	about 70
11 + 17	about 80
15 + 59	about 90
37 + 14	about 100

HINT Use estimation. Round up when the ones digit is 5 or more.
Round down when the ones digit is 4 or less.

Picture Clues

Honey studies chemistry. Her chemical concoctions can disintegrate a 180 kilogram metal ball!

If Honey disintegrates 8 metal balls, about how many balls are left?

_____

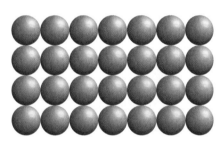

If Honey disintegrates 11 metal balls, about how many balls are left?

_____

 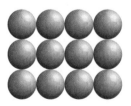

About how many more pink chem-balls are there than green chem-balls?

_____

_____

HINT Round up if the ones digit is 5 or more. Round down if the ones digit is 4 or less.

Matching

Wasabi uses his laser hands to cut off microbots from Yokai's control.

Match each subtraction statement with the best estimate. Round each number first. Then subtract to estimate the difference.

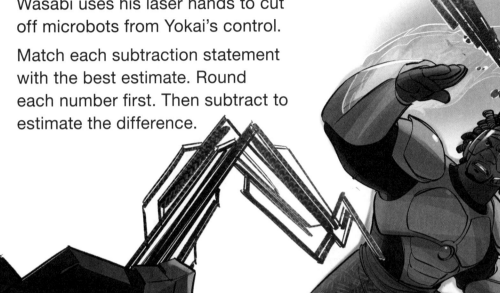

76 − 64	about 10
48 − 12	about 20
94 − 37	about 30
94 − 14	about 40
71 − 7	about 50
82 − 13	about 60
56 − 28	about 70
99 − 8	about 80
33 − 22	about 90

Puzzle Pieces

Joy and Sadness see hundreds of memories in Long Term Memory. All those memories sure add up!

Match each addition problem to its sum.

$$220 \\ + 211$$

856

$$598 \\ + 256$$

507

$$705 \\ + 151$$

638

$$325 \\ + 313$$

854

$$181 \\ + 326$$

431

Crack the Code

Riley has hundreds of memories that Joy helped create.

Calculate each sum. Then use the letter that matches each sum to crack the code.

Letter Code

$$236 + 310$$
K

$$492 + 433$$
C

$$227 + 381$$
G

$$512 + 273$$
I

$$366 + 622$$
E

$$562 + 304$$
N

$$128 + 754$$
P

$$675 + 126$$
A

$$489 + 201$$
D

$$823 + 151$$
T

$$184 + 577$$
S

$$764 + 283$$
R

What memory could Joy use to remind Riley of happier times?

___ ___ ___   ___ ___ ___ ___ ___ ___ ___
785 925 988   761 546 801 974 785 866 608

HINT You can use the place value chart on page 112 to help you.

Solve the Riddles

There are hundreds of memories in Long Term Memory! Forgetters send hundreds of old memories to the Memory Dump.

How many memories get dumped? Read the clues. Solve each riddle.

1. I am less than 90.

    I am an even number.

    I am 614 − 542.

    What number am I? _____

2. I am an odd number.

    I am 743 − 412.

    The sum of my digits is 7.

    What number am I? _____

3. I am 275 − 101.

    My tens digit is three more than my ones digit.

    I am more than 150.

    What number am I? _____

4. I am 54 rounded to the nearest 10.

    I am 331 − 281.

    I am an even number.

    What number am I? _____

5. I have 9 ones.

    The sum of my digits is 14.

    I am 843 − 334.

    What number am I? _____

HINT Solve the subtraction problem first. Use the other clues to check whether your answer is correct.

Crack the Code

Riley is dreaming about playing hockey when Anger has Dream Duty. Watch out everyone! Anger gets really worked up about hockey.

Calculate each difference. Then use the letter that matches each difference to crack the code.

Letter Code

875
− 234

T

554
− 490

B

189
− 127

A

771
− 356

E

750
− 576

L

962
− 445

K

708
− 422

M

327
− 236

D

536
− 159

I

289
− 161

H

612
− 561

O

347
− 208

N

What is a name for someone who gets angry easily?

___ ___ ___ ___ ___ ___ ___
128   51   641   128   415   62   91

Fill In the Blanks

Yokai shows up at Krei's press conference. Yokai attacks, unleashing hundreds and hundreds of microbots!

Use estimation to complete each addition statement. Round each number to the nearest 100. Then add to estimate the sum.

83 + 807 = about _____

625 + 118 = about _____

281 + 69 = about _____

516 + 233 = about _____

171 + 115 = about _____

146 + 265 = about _____

591 + 230 = about _____

735 + 160 = about _____

462 + 130 = about _____

250 + 654 = about _____

868 + 50 = about _____

550 + 201 = about _____

Use estimation to complete each subtraction statement. Round each number to the nearest 100. Then subtract to estimate the difference.

866 − 78 = about _____

694 − 408 = about _____

824 − 355 = about _____

405 − 135 = about _____

340 − 147 = about _____

955 − 856 = about _____

799 − 595 = about _____

557 − 200 = about _____

998 − 856 = about _____

636 − 224 = about _____

694 − 352 = about _____

724 − 169 = about _____

HINT When the number in the tens place is 5 or more, round up.
When it is 4 or less, round down.

Matching

On their first night in their new home, Riley's family buys take-out for dinner. They could have used a combination of bills and coins to pay for it.

Match each group of money to the correct total.

$6.30

$7.25

$2.35

$5.75

HINT Determine the value of each combination of coins first. Then match them to the dollar amount.

Crack the Code

Some of Riley's happy memories are about skating in winter. Winter just might be her favourite season!

Determine the amount of money in each group. Then write in the letter that matches each amount to crack the code.

Letter Code

   A

   T      H

   E

   L

   F

If money grew on trees, what would everyone's favourite season be?

___ ___ ___   ___ ___ ___ ___
$0.65 $0.85 $1.05 $3.35 $4.45 $7.15 $7.15

HINT Use skip counting to count the coins. Count by 5s for nickels, 10s for dimes, and 25s for quarters.

49

Solve the Riddles

Honey, Go Go, Wasabi, and Fred visit Hiro at the Lucky Cat Café.

Everyone decides to have a snack.

Snack Menu

Veggies and dip • • • • • **$2.80**

Cheese plate • • • • • • • **$2.65**

Fruit salad • • • • • • • • • • **$1.99**

Cookie • • • • • • • • • • • • • **$1.20**

Milk • • • • • • • • • • • • • • • • • **$0.90**

1. Imagine that Honey has 4 coins that add up to $4.25.

   What coins does Honey have? _____

   _____

   Does she have enough to buy a fruit salad and a cookie? _____

HINT There is only one combination of 4 coins that adds up to $4.25.

2. Imagine that Go Go has a bill and 4 coins that add up to $5.20.

   What bill and coins does Go Go have? _____

   _____

   Does she have enough to buy a cheese
   plate for now and a cheese plate for later? _____

3. Imagine that Wasabi has the same amount of money as
   Honey and Go Go together.

   How much money does Wasabi have? _____

   Does he have enough to buy veggies
   and dip, a cheese plate, and fruit salad? _____

4. Imagine that Fred has 1 bill and 10 coins. His bills and
   coins are all the same as Go Go's.

   How much money does Fred have? _____

   What bill and coins does he have? _____

   _____

   Does he have enough to buy a
   cheese plate, a fruit salad, and milk? _____

Word Problems

Baymax catches a ride on the trolley car to follow a microbot.

1. Baymax boards the trolley. Imagine that he has $2.00. If the trolley costs $1.25, how much does he have left?

   _____

2. Imagine that Baymax has 5 coins. They are all the same type of coin. The total is more than $1.00. The coins are not loonies or toonies.

   What coins does Baymax have? _____

   How much money does he have? _____

   If he rides the trolley again, how much money will he have left? _____

3. Imagine that Baymax finds 4 coins. The coins total $0.30.

   What coins does Baymax have? _____

   _____

   How much more money does he need for another trolley ride?

   _____

HINT You can cut out the coins on page 113 to help you.

Picture Clues

Hiro buys tools and parts to build his robots.
Imagine that Hiro has $8.00.

$2.85

$6.75

$4.95

$4.25

How much will he have left if he buys
the screwdriver?

_____

How much will he have left if he buys
the wrench?

_____

How much will he have left if he buys
the spool of wire?

_____

How much will he have left if he buys the
wire and pliers?

_____

How much more does the wrench cost than
the screwdriver?

_____

How much more does the screwdriver cost
than the pliers?

_____

HINT Add the cost of the items, then subtract the total from $8.00.

Picture Clues

Hundreds of Hiro's microbots join together to form a hand.

Write the multiplication sentence for each array of microbots.

_____

_____

_____

_____

HINT You can use the multiplication chart on page 112 to help you.

Crossword

Fred's armour has 3 claws on each of his 4 hands and feet. Altogether he has 12 claws.

Solve each multiplication fact. Write the word for each number. Complete the crossword.

Down	**Across**
1. 6 × 7 = _____	2. 5 × 2 = _____
3. 3 × 3 = _____	5. 4 × 4 = _____
4. 3 × 4 = _____	6. 2 × 4 = _____
7. 4 × 5 = _____	8. 6 × 3 = _____
	9. 7 × 1 = _____
	10. 5 × 6 = _____

HINT Make sure you spell number words like **four**, **thirty**, and **forty** correctly.

Crack the Code

Joy and Sadness learn to share responsibilities. They know it is best for Riley if they cooperate.

Solve each division sentence. Then use the letter that matches each quotient to crack the code.

Letter Code

4 ÷ 2 = _____ **T**   40 ÷ 5 = _____ **N**

9 ÷ 3 = _____ **K**   35 ÷ 5 = _____ **E**

7 ÷ 7 = _____ **M**   16 ÷ 4 = _____ **R**

16 ÷ 2 = _____ **S**   25 ÷ 5 = _____ **A**

18 ÷ 3 = _____ **O**   20 ÷ 2 = _____ **W**

What is another word for **cooperation**?

_____ _____ _____ _____ _____ _____ _____ _____
  2   7   5   1   10   6   4   3

HINT Think of dividing as sharing objects into equal groups.

56

Fill In the Blanks

Riley and Bing Bong divide and share their musical instruments. Twelve instruments divided between two people equals six instruments: $12 \div 2 = 6$.

Determine the missing numbers for each division sentence.

$42 \div 6 = \underline{\hspace{3em}}$ $16 \div 4 = \underline{\hspace{3em}}$

$\underline{\hspace{3em}} \div 2 = 5$ $\underline{\hspace{3em}} \div 5 = 6$

$35 \div \underline{\hspace{3em}} = 7$ $24 \div \underline{\hspace{3em}} = 8$

$21 \div 7 = \underline{\hspace{3em}}$ $10 \div 10 = \underline{\hspace{3em}}$

$\underline{\hspace{3em}} \div 3 = 8$ $\underline{\hspace{3em}} \div 6 = 2$

$18 \div \underline{\hspace{3em}} = 9$ $49 \div \underline{\hspace{3em}} = 7$

HINT Use your multiplication facts to help you figure out the missing number. For example, $2 \times 5 = 10$ helps solve $\underline{\hspace{3em}} \div 2 = 5$.

Function Box

Aunt Cass has a lot of cookies at her café. She could use multiplication to determine how many cookies she has. She could use division to decide how to display the cookies in an array.

How many cookies are there in this array?

_____

Write the multiplication sentence.

_____

How many cookies are there in this array?

_____

Write the multiplication sentence.

_____

Divide the 12 cookies into sets of 6.
Write the division sentence.

_____

Complete each equation. You can use the number line to help you.

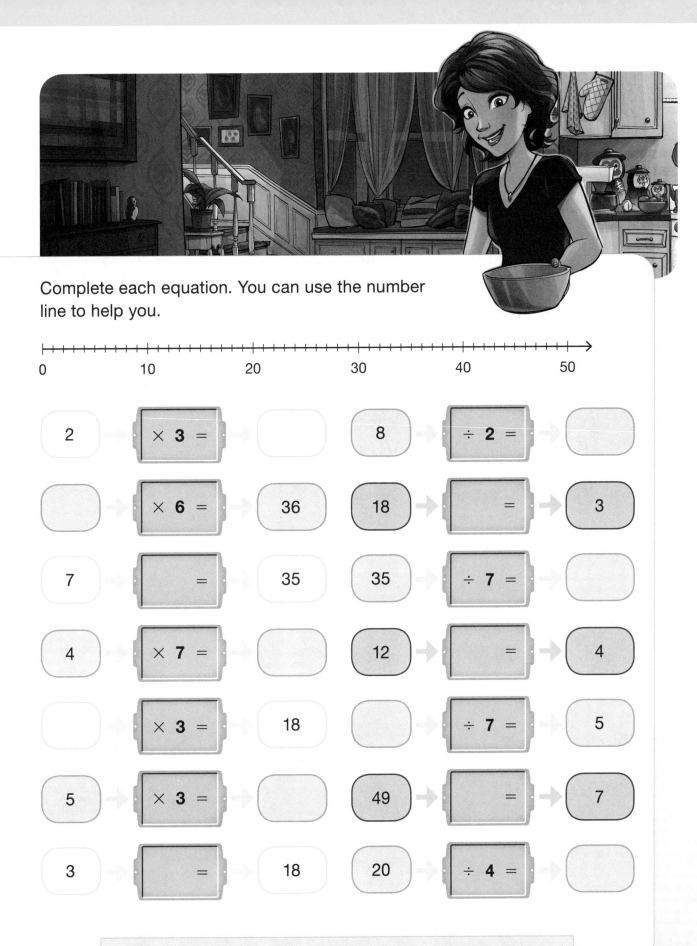

2 → × **3** = → ☐	8 → ÷ **2** = → ☐
☐ → × **6** = → 36	18 → **=** → 3
7 → **=** → 35	35 → ÷ **7** = → ☐
4 → × **7** = → ☐	12 → **=** → 4
☐ → × **3** = → 18	☐ → ÷ **7** = → 5
5 → × **3** = → ☐	49 → **=** → 7
3 → **=** → 18	20 → ÷ **4** = → ☐

HINT Use multiplication facts to determine the missing number.

Fill In the Blanks

Joy wants to fill the empty spaces on the Memory Shelf with happy memories. But the other Emotions want to add memories too.

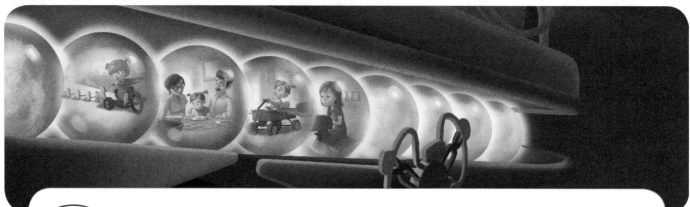

(Circle) the core of the pattern. What colours are the 3 memories that come next?

_____ _____ _____

Fill in the blanks to complete the patterns.

10, 20, _____, 40, 50

1, 4, 7, _____, 13

100, 95, 90, _____, 80

5, _____, 25, 35, 45

HINT Decide whether the pattern is repeating, growing, or shrinking. Then determine the missing term.

Colour to Complete

Patterns are everywhere. There is a pattern on Bing Bong's tie. There is a pattern on Riley's bag.

There are patterns in this 100-chart.

Skip count by 3s. Colour every third square red. The first square is coloured for you.

Skip count backward by 5s starting at 100. Circle every fifth square. The first square is circled for you.

1	2	3	4	5	6	7	8	9	10
11	12	13	14	15	16	17	18	19	20
21	22	23	24	25	26	27	28	29	30
31	32	33	34	35	36	37	38	39	40
41	42	43	44	45	46	47	48	49	50
51	52	53	54	55	56	57	58	59	60
61	62	63	64	65	66	67	68	69	70
71	72	73	74	75	76	77	78	79	80
81	82	83	84	85	86	87	88	89	90
91	92	93	94	95	96	97	98	99	100

HINT Patterns can grow (addition) or shrink (subtraction).

Function Box

Hiro wants to rebuild Baymax using the green nurse chip. He has to do some calculations first.

Check these calculations. Complete each equation.

5

12 → | + **9** = | →

25

6

17 → | = | → 13

2

31

27

18

21 → | − **9** = | →

28

39 → | = | → 23

23

37

5

34

0

14

22

+ **12** = | → 35

34 → | = | → 11

11

26

30

23

19

HINT Think of each question as either adding or subtracting.

Fill In the Blanks

Baymax asks Hiro to rate his pain on a scale of 1 to 10.

Use the numbers 1 to 10 to complete each equation. Both sides of the equation have to balance. Space is provided for you to show your work.

$22 - \underline{\qquad} = 9 + 10$

$24 - \underline{\qquad} = 8 + 7$

$15 - 11 = \underline{\qquad} - 2$

$6 + \underline{\qquad} = 16 - 4$

$8 + 19 = 17 + \underline{\qquad}$

$30 - \underline{\qquad} = 11 + 15$

$\underline{\qquad} + 18 = 20 + 7$

$18 - 8 = \underline{\qquad} + 5$

$9 + 6 = 24 - \underline{\qquad}$

$11 + 12 = 32 - \underline{\qquad}$

HINT Solve one side of the equation first. Then use addition and subtraction facts to determine the missing value.

Function Box

Members of Big Hero 6 need new armour. Hiro makes some calculations.

Check these calculations. Solve each equation.

4

20

× **0** =

45

100

× **0** =

99

598

× **0** =

780

291

× **0** =

What do you notice about the product when you multiply by 0?

_____

_____

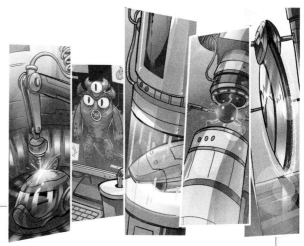

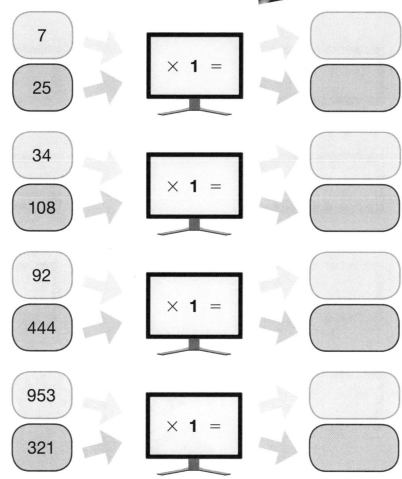

7		
25	× **1** =	
34		
108	× **1** =	
92		
444	× **1** =	
953		
321	× **1** =	

What do you notice about the product when you multiply by 1?

_____

_____

Fill In the Blanks

The Big Hero 6 need to make sure they are not being followed. Hiro is the first to arrive at the warehouse at 6:00. Each hero arrives 15 minutes after the previous hero. Then Yokai arrives 15 minutes after the last hero!

Write the arrival time for each person.

1. Hiro   :   AM / PM

2. Go Go   :   AM / PM

3. Wasabi   :   AM / PM

4. Baymax   :   AM / PM

5. Honey   :   AM / PM

6. Fred   :   AM / PM

7. Yokai   :   AM / PM

Picture Clues

Hiro comes home late. He has to sneak Baymax past Aunt Cass.

Each of these clocks shows time in the afternoon. Order these times from earliest to latest. The first one is done for you.

1

Order these times from latest to earliest.

 5:55 PM

 6:35 PM

 6:40 PM

 7:05 PM

HINT Read the time on each clock first. Then put them in order.

Fill In the Blanks

Joy keeps Sadness close to her as they journey through Long Term Memory. How long is Long Term Memory, anyway?

This ruler is 10 cm long. Use it to measure the length of each item. Write its length.

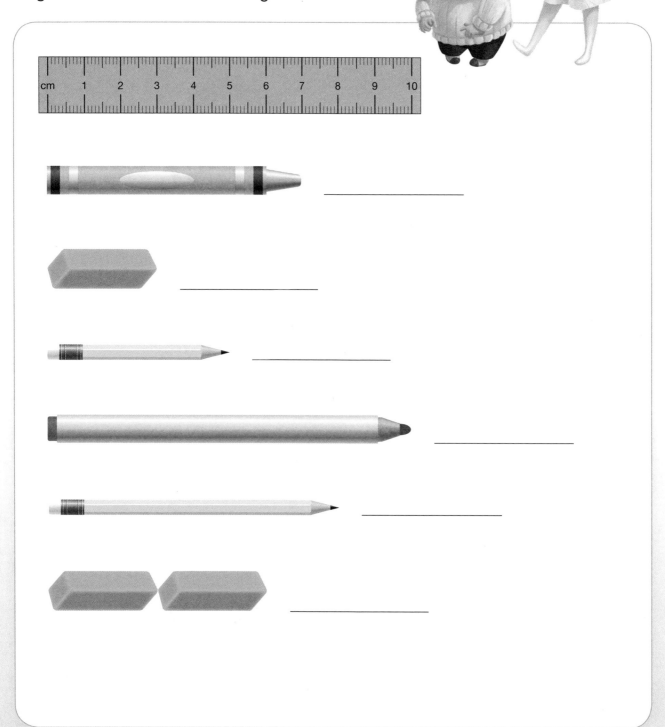

Matching

The Emotions are excited about the upgraded console in Headquarters. It is twice as long as the console they had before.

Match each description to the best height estimate.

height of a child	about 2 m
height of an adult	about 10 m
height of a car	about 170 cm
height of a house	about 130 cm

Match each description to the best width or length estimate.

width of a child's finger	about 14 km
distance between two towns	about 20 cm
length of a pencil	about 10 cm
length of a tube of toothpaste	about 1 cm

HINT There are 100 cm in 1 m. There are 1000 m in 1 km.

Fill In the Blanks

Sadness floats away on a cloud. Joy wants to go after Sadness. She uses the Imaginary Boyfriend Generator to create a tower of boyfriends.

Estimate the height of each Emotion's picture. Then measure its height in cm with a ruler.

estimate: _____

measurement: _____

estimate: _____

measurement: _____

estimate: _____

measurement: _____

estimate: _____

measurement: _____

HINT The width of your finger is about 1 cm. The width of your hand with your fingers spread out is about 10 cm.

Fill In the Blanks

Bing Bong shows Joy and Sadness the Train of Thought, which travels the perimeter of Riley's imagination.

Determine the perimeter and total area of each coloured area. Each square is 1 cm long.

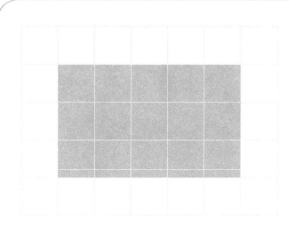

perimeter: _____

area: _____

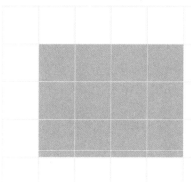

perimeter: _____

area: _____

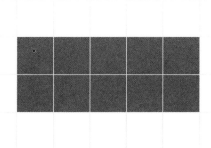

perimeter: _____

area: _____

perimeter: _____

area: _____

HINT **Perimeter** is the distance around a shape. **Area** is the number of square units needed to cover a shape.

Colour to Complete

Aunt Cass arranges the tables in the Lucky Cat Café.

The yellow area shows where the counter is. The grey area shows where the door opens. There are 10 square tables and 4 rectangular tables. Each square table is 1 cm² in the grid below. Each rectangular table is 2 cm² in the grid below. Colour the grid to show how you would arrange the tables.

Calculate the perimeter and area for the tables altogether.

perimeter: _____ cm   area: _____ cm²

Fill In the Blanks

Baymax can change his volume by deflating. This talent is handy when he needs to squeeze through a narrow window.

Write the volume of each object.

The volume of this cube is 1 cm³.

1 cm
1 cm
1 cm

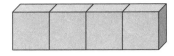

_____ cm³

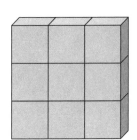

_____ cm³

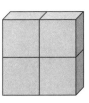

_____ cm³

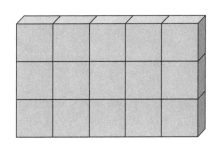

_____ cm³

HINT **Volume** is the space taken up by a 3-D object. The formula for volume is length × width × height. Its measurement is cubed.

Picture Clues

Riley gets frustrated answering her parents' questions. A cold, sweet drink of lemonade could help her cool down.

(Circle) the container that would hold the greater amount of lemonade.

1.

2.

3.

4.

5.

Colour to Complete

Riley uses different containers to make different sounds. Containers with different capacities make different sounds.

Each of these beakers has a different capacity.
Colour each beaker to show 250 mL.

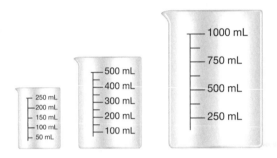

Use red to colour the containers that hold more than 500 mL. Use yellow to colour the containers that hold less than 500 mL.

HINT To measure capacity, you can use millilitres (mL) or litres (L). There are 1000 millilitres in 1 litre.

Fill In the Blanks

One microbot is so small and light, Hiro can hold it in his hand for a long time without getting tired.

Which would you use to measure the mass of each item: grams or kilograms?

bag of popcorn _____

watermelon _____

toothbrush _____

chocolate bar _____

eraser _____

bicycle _____

pencil _____

backpack with books inside _____

T-shirt _____

desk _____

letter _____

bag of potatoes _____

car _____

HINT Use grams to measure lighter objects. Use kilograms to measure heavier objects.

Maze

Who do you think is heavier: Hiro or Baymax?

Find your way through the maze. The correct path goes from the lightest object to the heaviest.

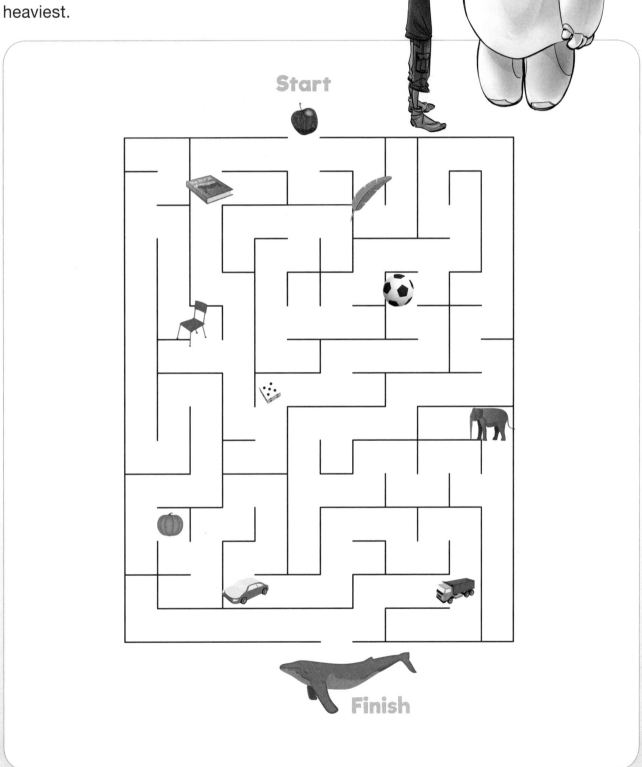

Start

Finish

Matching

Riley and her mom plan their day. They talk about when they will leave and when they will return.

Match each time period to the number of hours or minutes.

7:30 p.m. to 9:00 p.m.   5 hours

11:50 p.m. to 12:05 a.m.   60 hours

10:15 a.m. to 3:15 p.m.   15 minutes

Friday 8:00 a.m. to Sunday 8 p.m.   90 minutes

HINT There are 24 hours in one day. There are 60 minutes in one hour.

Matching

Riley's alarm woke her up too early! She doesn't need to wake up at 6:00 on a Saturday morning.

Match each time with the correct clock.

6:30

6:55

7:15

7:45

8:35

HINT When the shorter, hour hand is pointing between two numbers, always choose the lower number. For example, if it is pointing between 2 and 3, choose 2.

Fill In the Blanks

Riley misses skating on her outdoor rink in Minnesota. It's not cold enough to skate outside in San Francisco.

Write the temperature each thermometer shows.

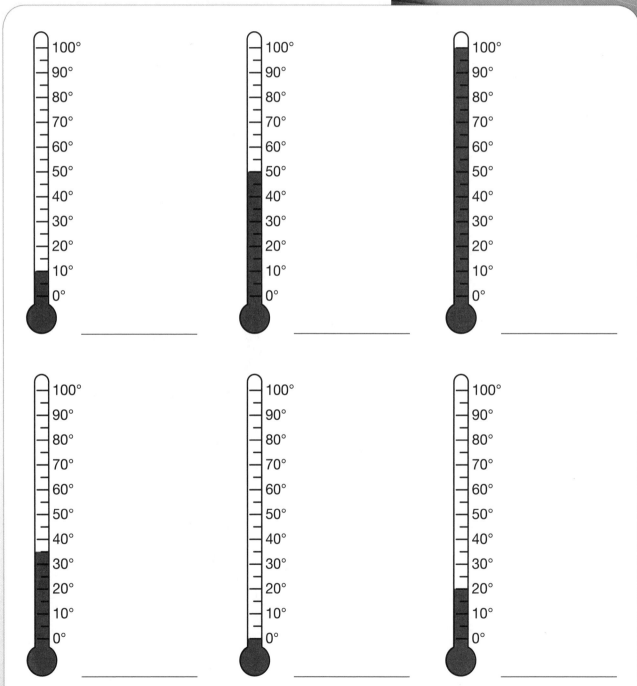

HINT Use the scale to determine the temperatures.

Colour to Complete

Yikes! Anger's body temperature starts to rise as he gets angry. There are flames coming out of his head!

Colour each thermometer with the correct temperature.

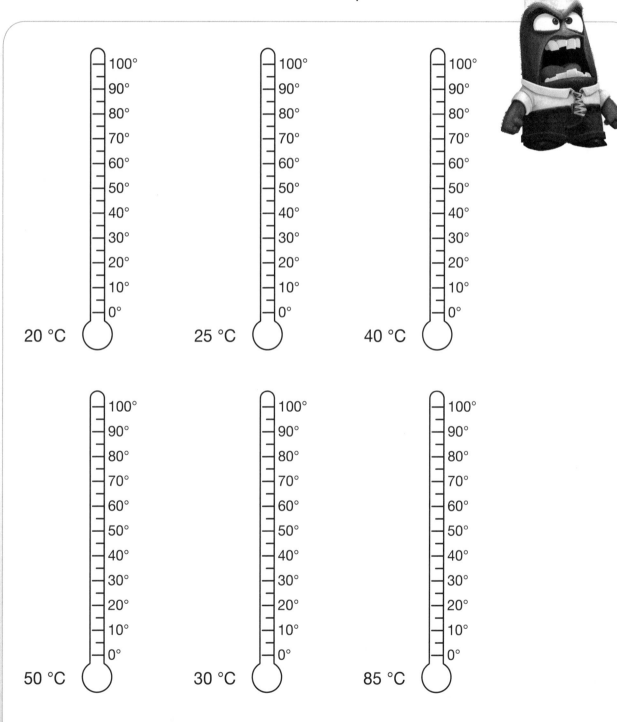

Colour to Complete

Riley has five Islands of Personality. One of the Islands is Goofball Island. There are many circles on Goofball Island.

What are your Islands of Personality? Draw one of the islands. Use shapes such as circles, triangles, hexagons, and trapezoids.

Matching

Joy draws a 2-D shape around Sadness.
She calls it the Circle of Sadness.

Match each 2-D shape to its name.

   triangle

                                        hexagon

   pentagon

                                        heptagon

                                        octagon

                                        rectangle

HINT **Tri-** means "three." Did you know that **penta-** means "five"? Find out what **hexa-**, **hepta-**, and **octa-** mean. Figure out how many sides those shapes have.

Matching

Abigail's uniform is symmetrical. Her pod is also symmetrical.

Make symmetrical shapes by matching the halves.

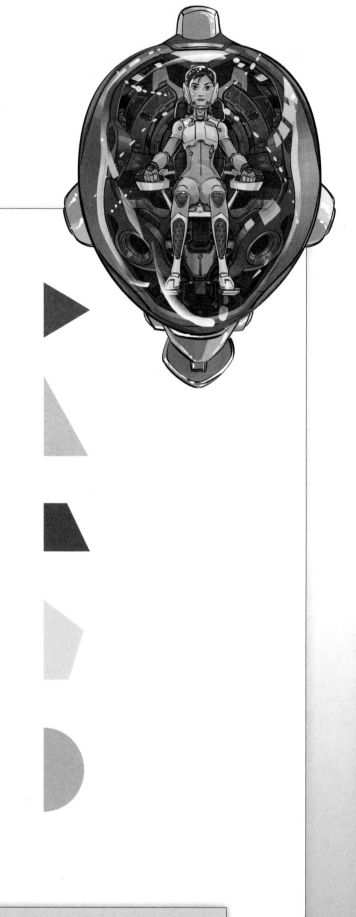

HINT An object is symmetrical when you can draw a line through it so that both halves are the same.

84

Picture Clues

Alistair Krei admires Hiro's microbots.

The microbots have 2 lines of symmetry.
Draw all the lines of symmetry on each shape.
How many lines of symmetry does each
shape have?

Colour to Complete

Joy and Sadness watch as Friendship Island falls into the Memory Dump. As it falls, it rotates.

Colour each letter. Use the Colour Key.

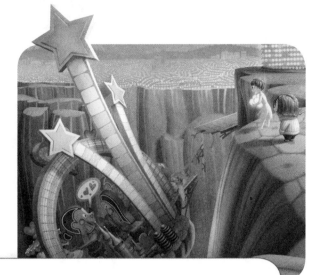

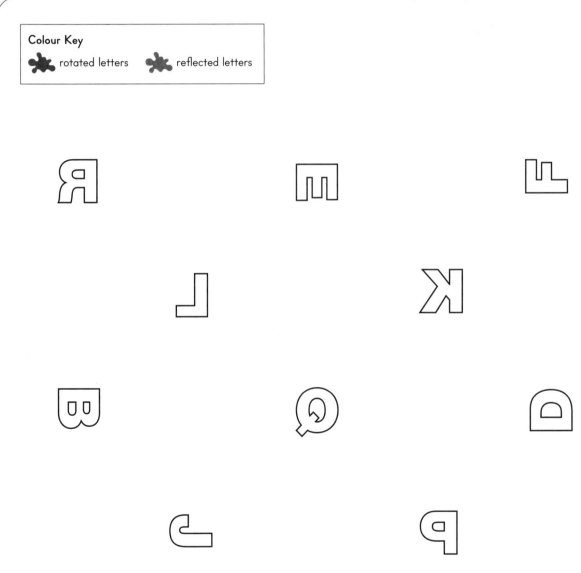

Colour Key

rotated letters   reflected letters

HINT **Reflecting** means flipping an object across a line.
Rotating means turning an object around.

Picture Clues

Riley is having a tough start to the day. First she wakes up early. Then she squirts toothpaste onto her reflection in the mirror!

How is each image transformed? Choose either **reflected** or **rotated**. The first one is done for you.

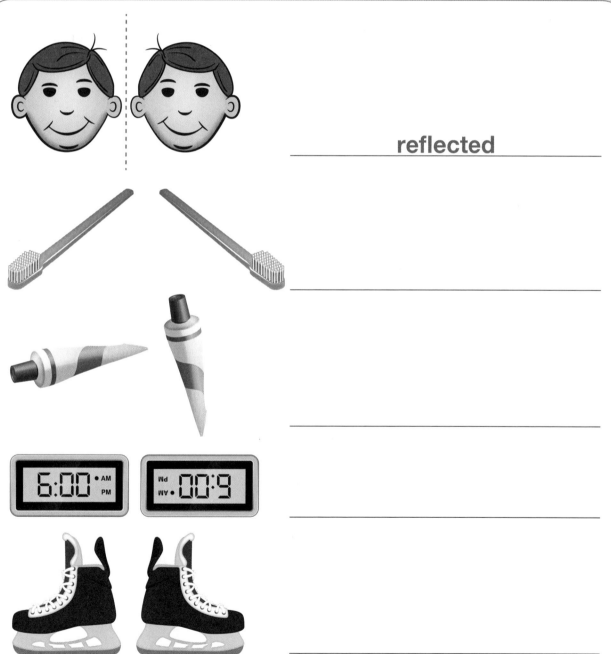

reflected

_____

_____

_____

_____

87

Picture Clues

Bing Bong, Joy, and Sadness change when they enter Abstract Thought. Now they have edges and vertices!

Complete the table. The first row is done for you.

3-D Object	Name	Number of Faces	Number of Edges	Number of Vertices
	cube	6	12	8

HINT A **vertex** is where two edges meet. An **edge** is where two faces meet. A **face** is the flat surface of a shape.

Solve the Riddles

Riley and Bing Bong set off on another adventure aboard their rocket ship. Part of the rocket ship is shaped like a rectangle-based prism.

Use the objects below to solve each riddle.

cube	rectangle-based prism	pentagon-based prism	square-based pyramid	trapezoid-based prism

1. I have 12 edges and 8 vertices.

   My edges are all the same length.

   What shape am I?

   _____

2. I have 8 edges and 5 vertices.

   I have square and triangular faces.

   What shape am I?

   _____

3. I have 12 edges and 8 vertices.

   My edges are not all equal in length.

   My top edges are the same length as my bottom edges.

   What shape am I?

   _____

4. I have 7 faces.

   5 of my faces are rectangles.

   What shape am I?

   _____

5. I have 6 faces.

   My edges are not all equal in length.

   What shape am I?

   _____

HINT Count the edges, vertices, and faces in each picture.

Matching

Professor Callaghan is very particular about who joins his team. He takes care to match students to his program during the Tech Showcase.

Sort these 3-D objects. Draw a line from each object to the correct part of the Venn diagram.

Six or More Vertices Square Base

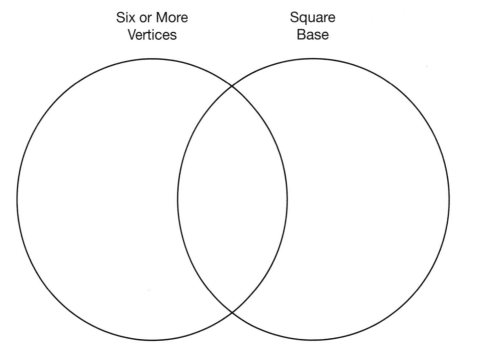

HINT You can use the 3-D object flash cards on page 115 to help you.

Fill In the Blanks

Hiro creates a robot no one has ever seen before. His microbots can form themselves into rectangle-based prisms.

Complete the table. The first row is done for you.

Prism	2-D Base	Number of Vertices	Number of Edges	Number of Faces
triangle-based prism	triangle	6	9	5
square-based prism				
rectangle-based prism				
hexagon-based prism				
octagon-based prism				

Picture Clues

Tadashi and Hiro race through the streets
of San Fransokyo.

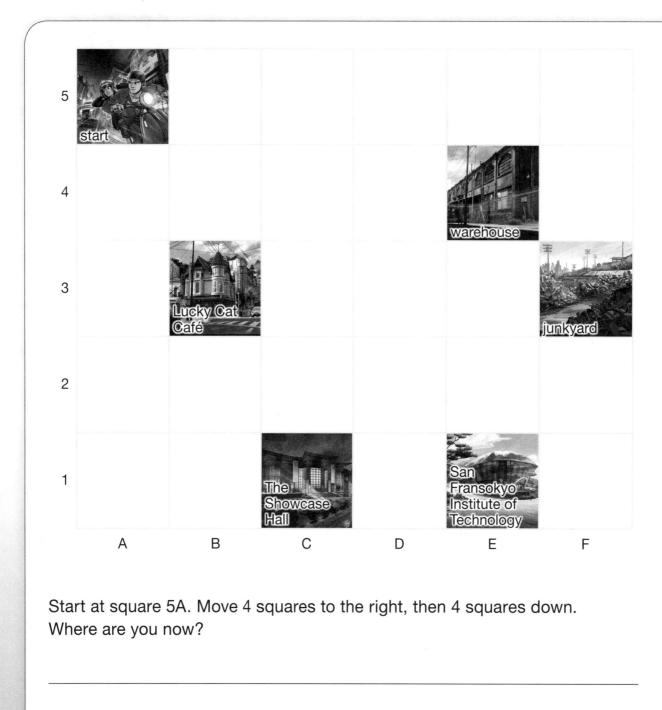

Start at square 5A. Move 4 squares to the right, then 4 squares down.
Where are you now?

_____

_____

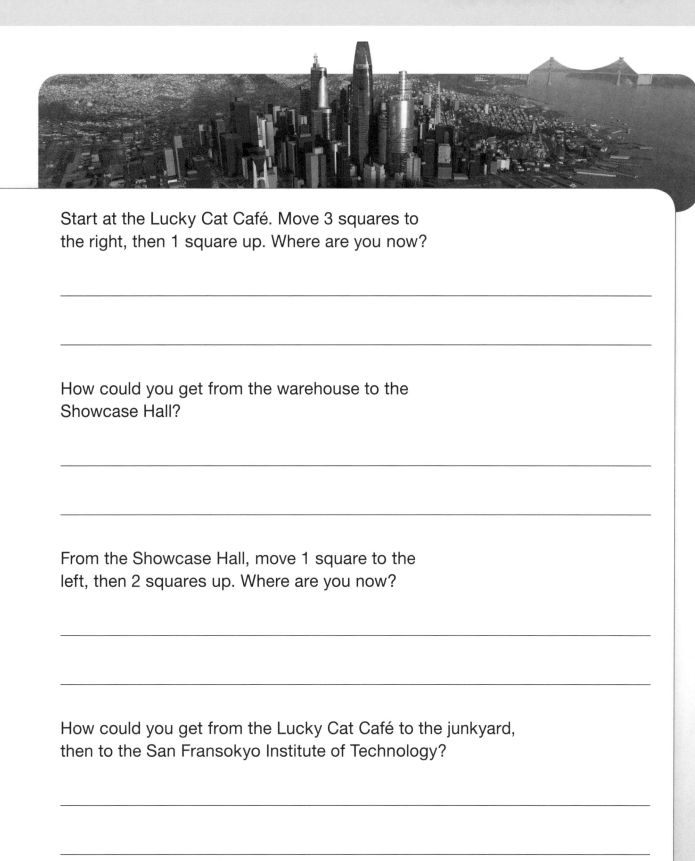

Start at the Lucky Cat Café. Move 3 squares to
the right, then 1 square up. Where are you now?

_____

_____

How could you get from the warehouse to the
Showcase Hall?

_____

_____

From the Showcase Hall, move 1 square to the
left, then 2 squares up. Where are you now?

_____

_____

How could you get from the Lucky Cat Café to the junkyard,
then to the San Fransokyo Institute of Technology?

_____

_____

HINT Use the letters and numbers to help you move around the map.

Picture Clues

Joy's bag is full of Riley's core memories. She pulls out a yellow happy core memory to share with Sadness.

There are 11 memories in this bag. Use the probability words to describe each situation.

Word Bank

impossible   unlikely   likely   certain

probability of selecting a purple memory: _____

probability of selecting a green memory: _____

probability of selecting a red memory: _____

probability of selecting
a yellow or blue memory: _____

probability of selecting a yellow,
blue, green, or purple memory: _____

HINT Think about the number of memories there are of each colour as well as the total number of memories.

Colour to Complete

As Joy drags Sadness through Long Term Memory, Sadness touches the memories. She turns them all blue.

Colour the bag of memories to show each situation.

From this bag, I am certain to select a blue memory.

From this bag, I am likely to select a red memory.

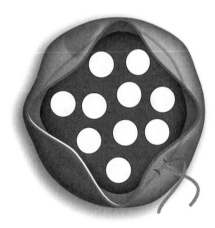

From this bag, I am unlikely to select a yellow memory.

From this bag, it is impossible for me to select a purple memory.

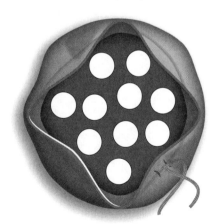

Graphing

Bing Bong cries candy tears. Some of the candies are wrapped. Some of them are unwrapped.

Count these candies. Complete the tally chart.

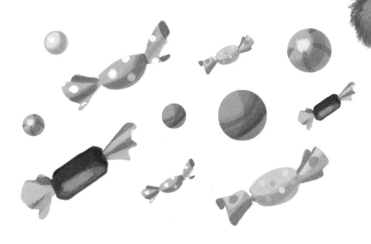

Wrapped Candies	Unwrapped Candies

Tally the candies according to another attribute.

HINT For your second tally chart, consider different attributes, such as size, shape, or colour.

96

Fill In the Blanks

Riley and her teammates work together to score goals in their hockey games. They could use a bar graph to keep track of their goals for 5 games.

Add a title and labels to this graph.

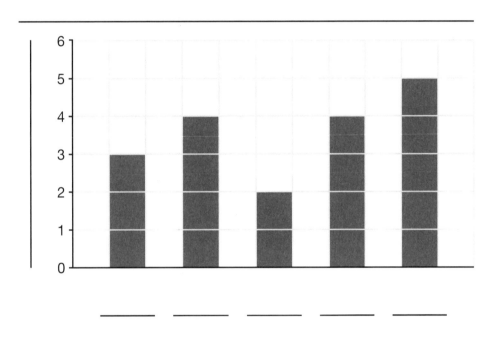

In which games did Riley's team score the same number of goals?

_____

_____

In 5 games, how many goals were there altogether? _____

_____

Graphing

Tadashi encourages Hiro to invent something to impress the judges at SFIT's Tech Showcase. Hiro invents microbots.

Examine the pictograph. Answer the questions.

Microbots Built in One Week

Monday

Tuesday

Wednesday

Thursday

Friday

Each ⬤ means 4 microbots.

How many microbots did Hiro build on Tuesday? _____

How many microbots did he build altogether? _____

On which day did he make the most microbots? _____

HINT Calculate how many microbots Hiro made each day. Then add them all together to determine the total.

Graphing

Aunt Cass sells many different smoothies at the Lucky Cat Café.

The tally chart shows how many smoothies of each flavour she sold.

Draw a bar graph to show the tally chart data. Make sure you give the graph a title, labels, and a scale.

pineapple	strawberry	cherry	banana	blueberry
卌	卌 卌 ||	卌 |||	卌 卌 卌	卌 卌

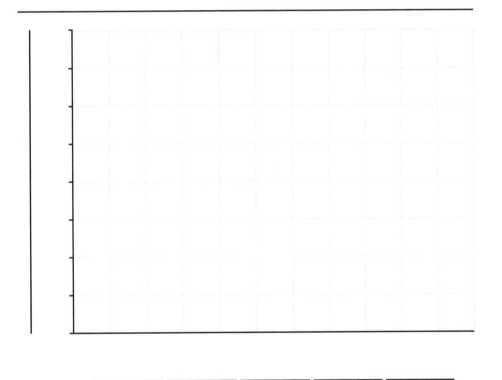

Read the bar graph. Which flavour of smoothie do customers buy the most?

Answers

Function Box

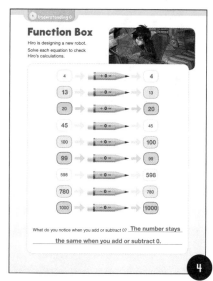

Hiro is designing a new robot.
Solve each equation to check
Hiro's calculations.

4	→	+ 0 =	→	4
13	→	– 0 =	→	13
20	→	+ 0 =	→	20
45	→	– 0 =	→	45
100	→	+ 0 =	→	100
99	→	– 0 =	→	99
598	→	+ 0 =	→	598
780	→	– 0 =	→	780
1000	→	– 0 =	→	1000

What do you notice when you add or subtract 0? __The number stays__
__the same when you add or subtract 0.__

Fill In the Blanks

The microbots are sucked backward into
the portal. Yokai slowly has fewer and fewer
microbots under his control.

Count backward by 10s from 50 to 0.
Fill in each missing number.

50, __40__ __30__ __20__ __10__ 0

Count backward by 10s from 95 to 25.
Fill in each missing number.

95, __85__ __75__ __65__ __55__ __45__ __35__ 25

Count backward by 5s from 70 to 40. Fill in each missing number.

70, __65__ __60__ __55__ __50__ __45__ 40

Count backward by 5s from 35 to 0. Fill in each missing number.

35, __30__ __25__ __20__ __15__ __10__ __5__ 0

Count backward by 2s from 54 to 38. Fill in each missing number.

54, __52__ __50__ __48__ __46__ __44__ __42__ __40__ 38

Count backward by 2s from 90 to 76. Fill in each missing number.

90, __88__ __86__ __84__ __82__ __80__ __78__ 76

HINT Look for the pattern in the ones digits as you
count backward by 2s, 5s, or 10s.

Crack the Code

Hiro and Baymax can't get out of
the portal.

Count backward in each pattern. Fill
in each missing number. Then use the
letter that matches each number to
crack the code. The first one is done
for you.

100, 90, __80__ 70, 60, 50, 40, __30__
· · · · · · · · · R · · · · · · · · · · · · T

75, 70, __65__ 60, 55, 50, __45__ 40
· · · · · · · · S · · · · · · · · · · · · C

20, 18, __16__ 14, 12, 10, 8, __4__
· · · · · · · · T · · · · · · · · · · · · O

40, 35, 30, __25__ 20, 15, __10__ 5
· · · · · · · · · · · · K · · · · · · · · I

60, 50, __40__ 30, 20, 10, __0__
· · · · · · · · · H

__58__ 56, 54, __52__ 50, 48, __46__ 44
· S · · · · · · · · E

What does Baymax use to save Hiro?

__H__ __I__ __S__   __R__ __O__ __C__ __K__ __E__ __T__
40 58 65   80   4   45 25 46 30

__F__ __I__ __S__ __T__
0   10 52 16

HINT Determine the pattern first to decide by how much to count backward.

Matching

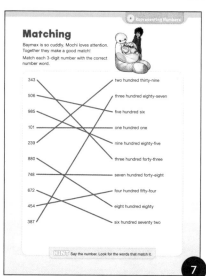

Baymax is so cuddly. Mochi loves attention.
Together they make a good match!

Match each 3-digit number with the correct
number word.

343		two hundred thirty-nine
506		three hundred eighty-seven
985		five hundred six
101		one hundred one
239		nine hundred eighty-five
880		three hundred forty-three
748		seven hundred forty-eight
672		four hundred fifty-four
454		eight hundred eighty
387		six hundred seventy two

HINT Say the number. Look for the words that match it.

Word Search

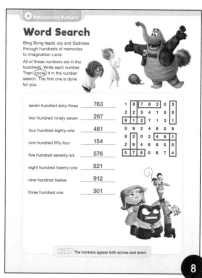

Bing Bong leads Joy and Sadness
through hundreds of memories
to Imagination Land.

All of these numbers are in the
hundreds. Write each number.
Then circle it in the number
search. The first one is done
for you.

seven hundred sixty-three	763
two hundred ninety-seven	297
four hundred eighty-one	481
one hundred fifty-four	154
five hundred seventy-six	576
eight hundred twenty-one	821
nine hundred twelve	912
three hundred one	301

```
1 8 7 6 3 0 3
2 2 3 4 1 5 0
9 1 2 7 1 3 1
0 9 2 4 6 0 9
8 2 0 2 4 8 1
2 9 4 6 8 5 5
5 7 6 0 8 7 4
```

HINT The numbers appear both across and down.

Maze

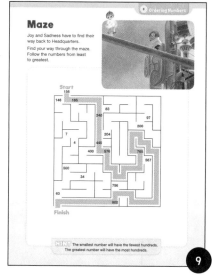

Joy and Sadness have to find their
way back to Headquarters.

Find your way through the maze.
Follow the numbers from least
to greatest.

Start
156

HINT The smallest number will have the fewest hundreds.
The greatest number will have the most hundreds.

Colour to Complete

From tallest to shortest, the Emotions are Joy,
Fear, Sadness, Disgust, and Anger.

Colour to order each set of numbers from greatest
to least. Use yellow for the greatest number,
followed by purple, blue, green, and red.

112 120 121 102 201

444 440 404 449 500

793 397 735 573 377

698 809 986 869 766

533 352 325 532 235

HINT Compare the hundreds digits first, then the tens, and then
the ones to determine the order of the numbers.

Fill In the Blanks

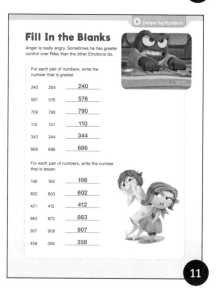

Anger is really angry. Sometimes he has greater
control over Riley than the other Emotions do.

For each pair of numbers, write the
number that is greater.

240	204	__240__
567	576	__576__
709	790	__790__
110	101	__110__
343	344	__344__
668	686	__686__

For each pair of numbers, write the number
that is lesser.

106	160	__106__
602	603	__602__
421	412	__412__
863	873	__863__
907	909	__907__
458	358	__358__

Crack the Code

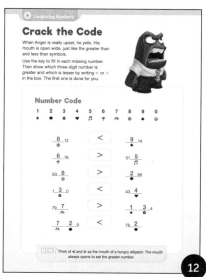

When Anger is really upset, he yells. His
mouth is open wide, just like the greater
and less than symbols.

Use the key to fill in each missing number.
Then show which three-digit number is
greater and which is lesser by writing < or >
in the box. The first one is done for you.

Number Code

1	2	3	4	5	6	7	8	9	0
★	●	✿	♥	♫	✚	❄	❀	♠	☺

__8__ 12	<	__9__ 14
__6__ 76	>	51 __5__
93 __8__	>	__2__ 86
__1__ __3__ 0	<	43 __4__
79 __7__	>	__1__ __3__
__7__ __2__ 9	<	78 __2__

HINT Think of < and > as the mouth of a hungry alligator. The mouth
always opens to eat the greater number.

*Sample answers provided.

Picture Clues

Fear sees 20 memories on the Memory Shelves.

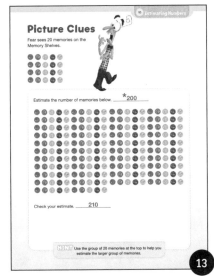

Estimate the number of memories below. *200

Check your estimate. 210

HINT Use the group of 20 memories at the top to help you estimate the larger group of memories.

13

Graphing

Go Go likes to chew gum while she works on her maglev bicycle.

Use this graph to estimate how many pieces of each flavour gum she has.

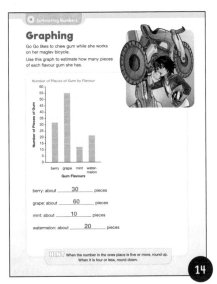

Number of Pieces of Gum by Flavour

berry: about 30 pieces

grape: about 60 pieces

mint: about 10 pieces

watermelon: about 20 pieces

HINT When the number in the ones place is five or more, round up. When it is four or less, round down.

14

Colour to Complete

Tadashi takes Hiro to the university to convince him to stop wasting his time on bot fights.

What are the school's initials? To find out, colour the picture. Use the Colour Key.

15

Matching

The Big Hero 6 realize that if they want to defeat Yokai, they have to divide up his microbots. Each hero takes on a sixth of the microbots.

Match each fraction with the correct picture.

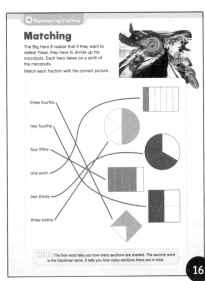

three fourths

two fourths

four fifths

one sixth

two thirds

three sixths

HINT The first word tells you how many sections are shaded. The second word is the fractional name. It tells you how many sections there are in total.

16

Colour to Complete

Wasabi lays out his tools so he can clearly see each one. One third of Wasabi's wrenches are blue.

Show each fraction. Colour the correct number of wrenches.

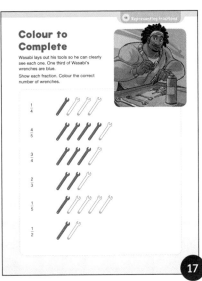

$\frac{1}{4}$

$\frac{4}{5}$

$\frac{3}{4}$

$\frac{2}{3}$

$\frac{1}{5}$

$\frac{1}{2}$

17

Colour to Complete

Riley is drawing a picture of her trip to Australia. She starts by dividing a piece of paper into thirds for the sky, water, and land.

Divide and colour the squares to show each fraction.

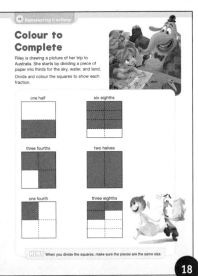

one half

six eighths

three fourths

two halves

one fourth

three eighths

HINT When you divide the squares, make sure the pieces are the same size.

18

Picture Clues

Riley's Emotions have some features in common. Other features are different.

Use fractions to describe the Emotions. Write the fractions out in words or numbers.

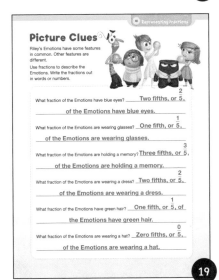

What fraction of the Emotions have blue eyes? Two fifths, or $\frac{2}{5}$, of the Emotions have blue eyes.

What fraction of the Emotions are wearing glasses? One fifth, or $\frac{1}{5}$, of the Emotions are wearing glasses.

What fraction of the Emotions are holding a memory? Three fifths, or $\frac{3}{5}$, of the Emotions are holding a memory.

What fraction of the Emotions are wearing a dress? Two fifths, or $\frac{2}{5}$, of the Emotions are wearing a dress.

What fraction of the Emotions have green hair? One fifth, or $\frac{1}{5}$, of the Emotions have green hair.

What fraction of the Emotions are wearing a hat? Zero fifths, or $\frac{0}{5}$, of the Emotions are wearing a hat.

19

Colour to Complete

It is pizza night! Riley wants to make sure there is no broccoli on her slices of pizza.

Divide each pizza. Then draw the toppings.

Draw pepperoni on four fourths of the pizza.

Draw broccoli on one half of the pizza.

Draw olives on two fourths of the pizza.

Draw peppers on one fourth of the pizza.

Draw pineapple on three fourths of the pizza.

Draw mushrooms on one eighth of the pizza.

Draw ham on two eighths of the pizza.

HINT Make sure that when you divide the pizza, all the slices are the same size.

20   **21**

*Sample answers provided.

Answwers

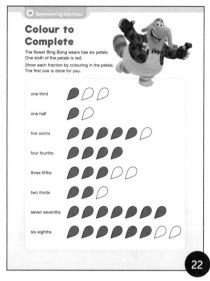

Colour to Complete

The flower Bing Bong wears has six petals.
One sixth of the petals is red.
Show each fraction by colouring in the petals.
The first one is done for you.

- one third
- one half
- five sixths
- four fourths
- three fifths
- two thirds
- seven sevenths
- six eighths

22

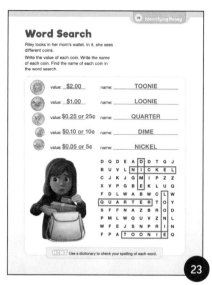

Word Search

Riley looks in her mom's wallet. In it, she sees different coins.

Write the value of each coin. Write the name of each coin in the word search. Find the name of each coin in the word search.

value: $2.00   name: TOONIE
value: $1.00   name: LOONIE
value: $0.25 or 25¢   name: QUARTER
value: $0.10 or 10¢   name: DIME
value: $0.05 or 5¢   name: NICKEL

```
D Q D E A D D T G J
B U V L N I C K E L
C J K J G M I P Z Z
X V P G B E K L U Q
F D L W A B W C L W
Q U A R T E R T O Y
S F F N A Z B R O D
P M L W Q U V Z N L
W F E J S N P R I N
F P A T O O N I E Q
```

HINT Use a dictionary to check your spelling of each word.

23

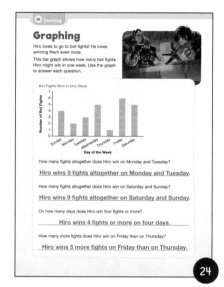

Graphing

Hiro loves to go to bot fights! He loves winning them even more.

This bar graph shows how many bot fights Hiro might win in one week. Use the graph to answer each question.

Bot Fights Won in One Week

How many fights altogether does Hiro win on Monday and Tuesday?

Hiro wins 5 fights altogether on Monday and Tuesday.

How many fights altogether does Hiro win on Saturday and Sunday?

Hiro wins 9 fights altogether on Saturday and Sunday.

On how many days does Hiro win four fights or more?

Hiro wins 4 fights or more on four days.

How many more fights does Hiro win on Friday than on Thursday?

Hiro wins 5 more fights on Friday than on Thursday.

24

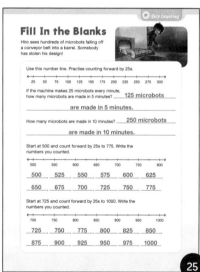

Fill In the Blanks

Hiro sees hundreds of microbots falling off a conveyor belt into a barrel. Somebody has stolen his design!

Use this number line. Practise counting forward by 25s.

25 50 75 100 125 150 175 200 225 250 275 300

If the machine makes 25 microbots every minute, how many microbots are made in 5 minutes? **125 microbots are made in 5 minutes.**

How many microbots are made in 10 minutes? **250 microbots are made in 10 minutes.**

Start at 500 and count forward by 25s to 775. Write the numbers you counted.

500 550 600 650 700 750 800

| 500 | 525 | 550 | 575 | 600 | 625 |
| 650 | 675 | 700 | 725 | 750 | 775 |

Start at 725 and count forward by 25s to 1000. Write the numbers you counted.

700 750 800 850 900 950 1000

| 725 | 750 | 775 | 800 | 825 | 850 |
| 875 | 900 | 925 | 950 | 975 | 1000 |

25

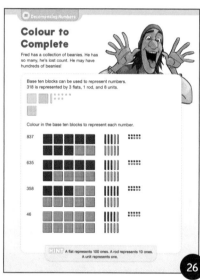

Colour to Complete

Fred has a collection of beanies. He has so many, he's lost count. He may have hundreds of beanies!

Base ten blocks can be used to represent numbers. 318 is represented by 3 flats, 1 rod, and 8 units.

Colour in the base ten blocks to represent each number.

- 837
- 635
- 358
- 46

HINT A flat represents 100 ones. A rod represents 10 ones. A unit represents one.

26

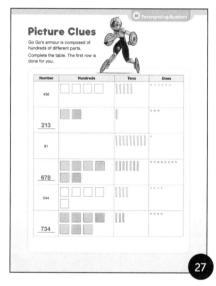

Picture Clues

Go Go's armour is composed of hundreds of different parts.
Complete the table. The first row is done for you.

Number	Hundreds	Tens	Ones
456			
213			
91			
678			
544			
734			

27

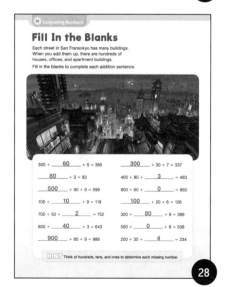

Fill In the Blanks

Each street in San Fransokyo has many buildings. When you add them up, there are hundreds of houses, offices, and apartment buildings.
Fill in the blanks to complete each addition sentence.

300 + **60** + 5 = 365   **300** + 30 + 7 = 337
80 + 3 = 83   400 + 80 + **3** = 483
500 + 90 + 9 = 599   800 + 60 + **0** = 860
100 + **10** + 9 = 119   **100** + 20 + 6 = 126
700 + 50 + **2** = 752   300 + **80** + 9 = 389
600 + **40** + 3 = 643   500 + **0** + 8 = 508
900 + 80 + 9 = 989   200 + 30 + **4** = 234

HINT Think of hundreds, tens, and ones to determine each missing number.

28

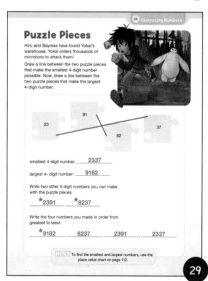

Puzzle Pieces

Hiro and Baymax have found Yokai's warehouse. Yokai orders thousands of microbots to attack them!

Draw a line between the two puzzle pieces that make the smallest 4-digit number possible. Now, draw a line between the two puzzle pieces that make the largest 4-digit number.

91   23   82   37

smallest 4-digit number: **2337**

largest 4-digit number: **9182**

Write two other 4-digit numbers you can make with the puzzle pieces.

*2391   *8237

Write the four numbers you made in order from greatest to least.

*9182   8237   2391   2337

HINT To find the smallest and largest numbers, use the place value chart on page 112.

29

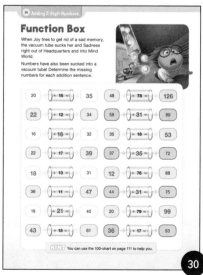

Function Box

When Joy tries to get rid of a sad memory, the vacuum tube sucks her and Sadness right out of Headquarters and into Mind World.

Numbers have also been sucked into a vacuum tube! Determine the missing numbers for each addition sentence.

20 + **15** = 35   48 + **78** = 126
22 + **12** = 34   58 + **31** = 89
16 + **16** = 32   35 + **18** = 53
22 + **17** = 39   37 + **35** = 72
18 + **13** = 31   12 + **76** = 88
36 + **11** = 47   44 + **31** = 75
19 + **21** = 40   20 + **79** = 99
43 + **18** = 61   36 + **17** = 53

HINT You can use the 100-chart on page 111 to help you.

30

*Sample answers provided.

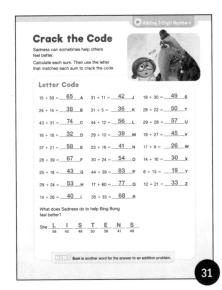

Crack the Code (31)

Sadness can sometimes help others feel better.
Calculate each sum. Then use the letter that matches each sum to crack the code.

Letter Code

15 + 50 = **65** A	31 + 11 = **42** J	19 + 30 = **49** S
24 + 14 = **38** B	31 + 5 = **36** K	28 + 22 = **50** T
43 + 31 = **74** C	44 + 12 = **56** L	29 + 28 = **57** U
16 + 16 = **32** D	29 + 10 = **39** M	18 + 27 = **45** V
37 + 21 = **58** E	23 + 18 = **41** N	17 + 9 = **26** W
28 + 39 = **67** F	30 + 24 = **54** O	14 + 16 = **30** X
25 + 18 = **43** G	44 + 39 = **83** P	6 + 13 = **19** Y
29 + 24 = **53** H	17 + 60 = **77** Q	12 + 21 = **33** Z
14 + 26 = **40** I	35 + 33 = **68** R	

What does Sadness do to help Bing Bong feel better?

She **L I S T E N S**
56 40 49 50 58 41 49

HINT Sum is another word for the answer to an addition problem.

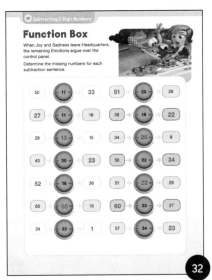

Function Box (32)

When Joy and Sadness leave Headquarters, the remaining Emotions argue over the control panel.
Determine the missing numbers for each subtraction sentence.

50 → 17 → 33
51 → 23 → 28

27 → 11 → 16
38 → 16 → 22

28 → 13 → 15
34 → 25 → 9

43 → 20 → 23
56 → 22 → 34

52 → 16 → 36
51 → 22 → 29

65 → 50 → 15
60 → 33 → 27

24 → 23 → 1
57 → 34 → 23

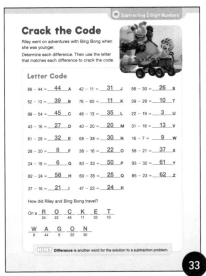

Crack the Code (33)

Riley went on adventures with Bing Bong when she was younger.
Determine each difference. Then use the letter that matches each difference to crack the code.

Letter Code

88 − 44 = **44** A	42 − 11 = **31** J	56 − 30 = **26** S
52 − 13 = **39** B	76 − 65 = **11** K	39 − 29 = **10** T
99 − 54 = **45** C	48 − 13 = **35** L	22 − 19 = **3** U
43 − 16 = **27** D	40 − 20 = **20** M	31 − 18 = **13** V
61 − 29 = **32** E	68 − 38 = **30** N	16 − 7 = **9** W
28 − 20 = **8** F	38 − 16 = **22** O	58 − 21 = **37** X
24 − 18 = **6** G	83 − 33 = **50** P	93 − 32 = **61** Y
82 − 24 = **58** H	60 − 35 = **25** Q	85 − 23 = **62** Z
37 − 16 = **21** I	47 − 23 = **24** R	

How did Riley and Bing Bong travel?

On a **R O C K E T**
24 26 11 32 10

W A G O N
9 44 6 22 30

HINT Difference is another word for the solution to a subtraction problem.

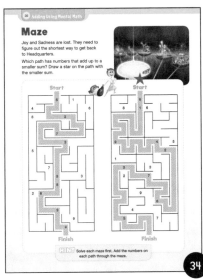

Maze (34)

Joy and Sadness are lost. They need to figure out the shortest way to get back to Headquarters.
Which path has numbers that add up to a smaller sum? Draw a star on the path with the smaller sum.

HINT Solve each maze first. Add the numbers on each path through the maze.

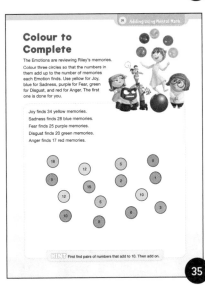

Colour to Complete (35)

The Emotions are reviewing Riley's memories.
Colour three circles so that the numbers in them add up to the number of memories each Emotion finds. Use yellow for Joy, blue for Sadness, purple for Fear, green for Disgust, and red for Anger. The first one is done for you.

Joy finds 34 yellow memories.
Sadness finds 28 blue memories.
Fear finds 25 purple memories.
Disgust finds 20 green memories.
Anger finds 17 red memories.

HINT First find pairs of numbers that add to 10. Then add on.

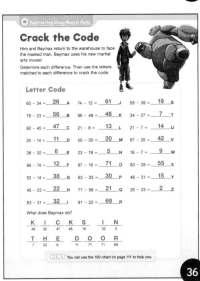

Crack the Code (36)

Hiro and Baymax return to the warehouse to face the masked man. Baymax uses his new martial arts moves!
Determine each difference. Then use the letters matched to each difference to crack the code.

Letter Code

60 − 34 = **26** A	74 − 13 = **61** J	58 − 39 = **19** S
79 − 23 = **56** B	96 − 48 = **48** K	34 − 27 = **7** T
92 − 45 = **47** C	21 − 8 = **13** L	21 − 7 = **14** U
25 − 14 = **11** D	50 − 30 = **20** M	67 − 25 = **42** V
38 − 32 = **6** E	23 − 18 = **5** N	16 − 7 = **9** W
86 − 74 = **12** F	87 − 16 = **71** O	83 − 28 = **55** X
52 − 14 = **38** G	63 − 33 = **30** P	46 − 31 = **15** Y
45 − 23 = **22** H	77 − 56 = **21** Q	25 − 23 = **2** Z
63 − 31 = **32** I	91 − 22 = **69** R	

What does Baymax do?

K I C K S   I N
48 32 47 48 19 5

T H E   D O O R
7   22 6   11 71 71 69

HINT You can use the 100-chart on page 111 to help you.

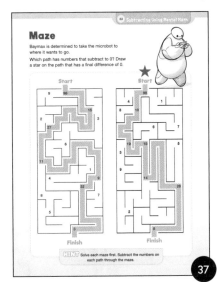

Maze (37)

Baymax is determined to take the microbot to where it wants to go.
Which path has numbers that subtract to 0? Draw a star on the path that has a final difference of 0.

HINT Solve each maze first. Subtract the numbers on each path through the maze.

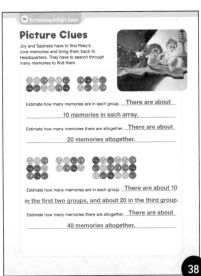

Picture Clues (38)

Joy and Sadness have to find Riley's core memories and bring them back to Headquarters. They have to search through many memories to find them.

Estimate how many memories are in each group. **There are about 10 memories in each array.**

Estimate how many memories there are altogether. **There are about 20 memories altogether.**

Estimate how many memories are in each group. **There are about 10 in the first two groups, and about 20 in the third group.**

Estimate how many memories there are altogether. **There are about 40 memories altogether.**

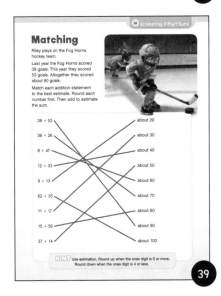

Matching (39)

Riley plays on the Fog Horns hockey team.
Last year the Fog Horns scored 38 goals. This year they scored 53 goals. Altogether they scored about 90 goals.
Match each addition statement to the best estimate. Round each number first. Then add to estimate the sum.

38 + 53	about 20
36 + 26	about 30
8 + 47	about 40
12 + 33	about 50
9 + 13	about 60
62 + 35	about 70
11 + 17	about 80
15 + 59	about 90
37 + 14	about 100

HINT Use estimation. Round up when the ones digit is 5 or more. Round down when the ones digit is 4 or less.

*Sample answers provided.

Answers

Picture Clues

Honey studies chemistry. Her chemical concoctions can disintegrate a 180 kilogram metal ball!

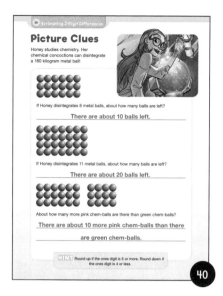

If Honey disintegrates 8 metal balls, about how many balls are left?

There are about 10 balls left.

If Honey disintegrates 11 metal balls, about how many balls are left?

There are about 20 balls left.

About how many more pink chem-balls are there than green chem-balls?

There are about 10 more pink chem-balls than there are green chem-balls.

HINT Round up if the ones digit is 5 or more. Round down if the ones digit is 4 or less.

40

Matching

Wasabi uses his laser hands to cut off microbots from Yokai's control.

Match each subtraction statement with the best estimate. Round each number first. Then subtract to estimate the difference.

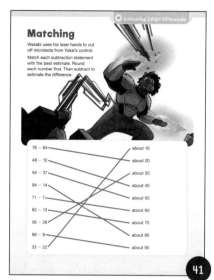

76 − 64 — about 10
48 − 12 — about 20
94 − 37 — about 30
94 − 14 — about 40
71 − 7 — about 50
82 − 13 — about 60
56 − 28 — about 70
99 − 8 — about 80
33 − 22 — about 90

41

Puzzle Pieces

Joy and Sadness see hundreds of memories in Long Term Memory. All those memories sure add up!

Match each addition problem to its sum.

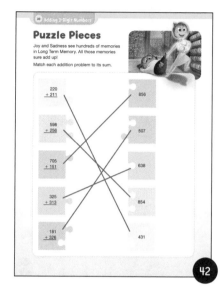

220 + 211 — 431
598 + 256 — 854
705 + 151 — 856
325 + 313 — 638
181 + 326 — 507

42

Crack the Code

Riley has hundreds of memories that Joy helped create.

Calculate each sum. Then use the letter that matches each sum to crack the code.

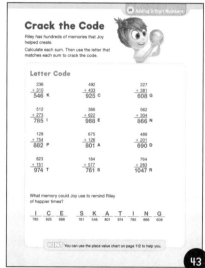

Letter Code

236 + 310 = 546 **K**	492 + 433 = 925 **C**	227 + 381 = 608 **G**
512 + 273 = 785 **I**	366 + 622 = 988 **E**	562 + 304 = 866 **N**
128 + 754 = 882 **P**	675 + 126 = 801 **A**	489 + 201 = 690 **D**
823 + 151 = 974 **T**	184 + 577 = 761 **S**	764 + 283 = 1047 **R**

What memory could Joy use to remind Riley of happier times?

I C E   S K A T I N G
785 925 988   761 546 801 974 785 866 608

HINT You can use the place value chart on page 112 to help you.

43

Solve the Riddles

There are hundreds of memories in Long Term Memory! Forgetters send hundreds of old memories to the Memory Dump.

How many memories get dumped? Read the clues. Solve each riddle.

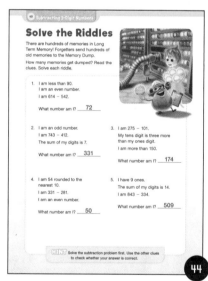

1. I am less than 90.
   I am an even number.
   I am 614 − 542.
   What number am I? **72**

2. I am an odd number.
   I am 743 − 412.
   The sum of my digits is 7.
   What number am I? **331**

3. I am 275 − 101.
   My tens digit is three more than my ones digit.
   I am more than 150.
   What number am I? **174**

4. I am 54 rounded to the nearest 10.
   I am 331 − 281.
   I am an even number.
   What number am I? **50**

5. I have 9 ones.
   The sum of my digits is 14.
   I am 843 − 334.
   What number am I? **509**

HINT Solve the subtraction problem first. Use the other clues to check whether your answer is correct.

44

Crack the Code

Riley is dreaming about playing hockey when Anger has Dream Duty. Watch out everyone! Anger gets really worked up about hockey.

Calculate each difference. Then use the letter that matches each difference to crack the code.

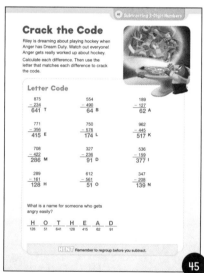

Letter Code

875 − 234 = 641 **T**	554 − 490 = 64 **B**	189 − 127 = 62 **A**
771 − 356 = 415 **E**	750 − 576 = 174 **L**	962 − 445 = 517 **K**
708 − 422 = 286 **M**	327 − 236 = 91 **D**	536 − 159 = 377 **I**
289 − 161 = 128 **H**	612 − 561 = 51 **O**	347 − 208 = 139 **N**

What is a name for someone who gets angry easily?

H O T H E A D
128 51 641 128 415 62 91

HINT Remember to regroup before you subtract.

45

Fill In the Blanks

Yokai shows up at Krei's press conference. Yokai attacks, unleashing hundreds and hundreds of microbots!

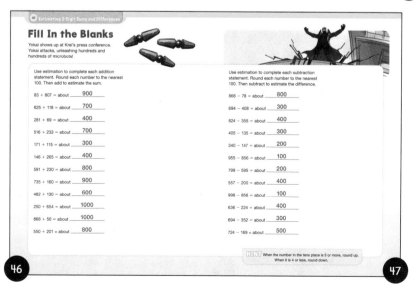

Use estimation to complete each addition statement. Round each number to the nearest 100. Then add to estimate the sum.

83 + 807 = about **900**
625 + 118 = about **700**
281 + 69 = about **400**
516 + 233 = about **700**
171 + 115 = about **300**
146 + 265 = about **400**
591 + 230 = about **800**
735 + 160 = about **900**
462 + 130 = about **600**
250 + 654 = about **1000**
868 + 50 = about **1000**
550 + 201 = about **800**

Use estimation to complete each subtraction statement. Round each number to the nearest 100. Then subtract to estimate the difference.

866 − 78 = about **800**
694 − 408 = about **300**
824 − 355 = about **400**
405 − 135 = about **300**
340 − 147 = about **200**
955 − 856 = about **100**
799 − 595 = about **200**
557 − 200 = about **400**
998 − 856 = about **100**
636 − 224 = about **400**
694 − 352 = about **300**
724 − 169 = about **500**

HINT When the number in the tens place is 5 or more, round up. When it is 4 or less, round down.

46 **47**

Matching

On their first night in their new home, Riley's family buys take-out for dinner. They could have used a combination of bills and coins to pay for it.

Match each group of money to the correct total.

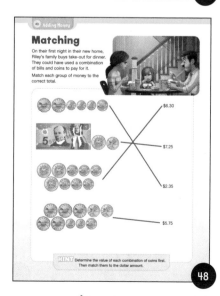

$6.30
$7.25
$2.35
$5.75

HINT Determine the value of each combination of coins first. Then match them to the dollar amount.

48

*Sample answers provided.

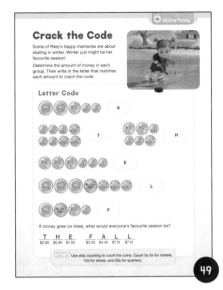

Crack the Code

Some of Riley's happy memories are about skating in winter. Winter just might be her favourite season!

Determine the amount of money in each group. Then write in the letter that matches each amount to crack the code.

Letter Code

A

T   H

E

L

F

If money grew on trees, what would everyone's favourite season be?

T H E   F A L L
$0.65 $0.85 $1.05 $3.35 $4.45 $7.15 $7.15

HINT Use skip counting to count the coins. Count by 5s for nickels, 10s for dimes, and 25s for quarters.

49

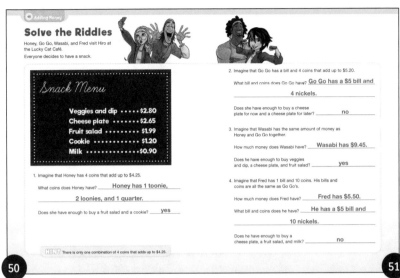

Solve the Riddles

Honey, Go Go, Wasabi, and Fred visit Hiro at the Lucky Cat Café.
Everyone decides to have a snack.

Snack Menu

Veggies and dip · · · · · $2.80
Cheese plate · · · · · · · $2.65
Fruit salad · · · · · · · · · $1.99
Cookie · · · · · · · · · · · · $1.20
Milk · · · · · · · · · · · · · · $0.90

1. Imagine that Honey has 4 coins that add up to $4.25.

What coins does Honey have?   **Honey has 1 toonie, 2 loonies, and 1 quarter.**

Does she have enough to buy a fruit salad and a cookie?   **yes**

2. Imagine that Go Go has a bill and 4 coins that add up to $5.20.

What bill and coins does Go Go have?   **Go Go has a $5 bill and 4 nickels.**

Does she have enough to buy a cheese plate for now and a cheese plate for later?   **no**

3. Imagine that Wasabi has the same amount of money as Honey and Go Go together.

How much money does Wasabi have?   **Wasabi has $9.45.**

Does he have enough to buy veggies and dip, a cheese plate, and fruit salad?   **yes**

4. Imagine that Fred has 1 bill and 10 coins. His bills and coins are all the same as Go Go's.

How much money does Fred have?   **Fred has $5.50.**

What bill and coins does he have?   **He has a $5 bill and 10 nickels.**

Does he have enough to buy a cheese plate, a fruit salad, and milk?   **no**

HINT There is only one combination of 4 coins that adds up to $4.25.

50   **51**

Word Problems

Baymax catches a ride on the trolley car to follow a microbot.

1. Baymax boards the trolley. Imagine that he has $2.00. If the trolley costs $1.25, how much does he have left?

He has $0.75 or 75¢ left.

2. Imagine that Baymax has 5 coins. They are all the same type of coin. The total is more than $1.00. The coins are not loonies or toonies.

What coins does Baymax have?   **Baymax has 5 quarters.**

How much money does he have?   **He has $1.25.**

If he rides the trolley again, how much money will he have left?   **He will have no money left.**

3. Imagine that Baymax finds 4 coins. The coins total $0.30.

What coins does Baymax have?   **Baymax has 2 dimes and 2 nickels.**

How much more money does he need for another trolley ride?

He needs $0.95 or 95¢ more.

HINT You can cut out the coins on page 113 to help you.

52

Picture Clues

Hiro buys tools and parts to build his robots. Imagine that Hiro has $8.00.

$2.85 $6.75 $4.95 $4.25

How much will he have left if he buys the screwdriver?   **$3.05**

How much will he have left if he buys the wrench?   **$1.25**

How much will he have left if he buys the spool of wire?   **$5.15**

How much will he have left if he buys the wire and pliers?   **$0.90 or 90¢**

How much more does the wrench cost than the screwdriver?   **$1.80**

How much more does the screwdriver cost than the pliers?   **$0.70 or 70¢**

HINT Add the cost of the items, then subtract the total from $8.00.

53

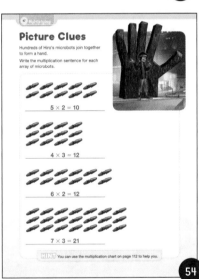

Picture Clues

Hundreds of Hiro's microbots join together to form a hand.

Write the multiplication sentence for each array of microbots.

$5 \times 2 = 10$

$4 \times 3 = 12$

$6 \times 2 = 12$

$7 \times 3 = 21$

HINT You can use the multiplication chart on page 112 to help you.

54

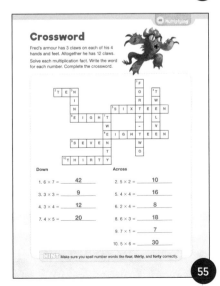

Crossword

Fred's armour has 3 claws on each of his 4 hands and feet. Altogether he has 12 claws.

Solve each multiplication fact. Write the word for each number. Complete the crossword.

Down

1. $6 \times 7 =$ **42**
3. $3 \times 3 =$ **9**
4. $3 \times 4 =$ **12**
7. $4 \times 5 =$ **20**

Across

2. $5 \times 2 =$ **10**
5. $4 \times 4 =$ **16**
6. $2 \times 4 =$ **8**
8. $6 \times 3 =$ **18**
9. $7 \times 1 =$ **7**
10. $5 \times 6 =$ **30**

HINT Make sure you spell number words like **four, thirty,** and **forty** correctly.

55

Crack the Code

Joy and Sadness learn to share responsibilities. They know it is best for Riley if they cooperate.

Solve each division sentence. Then use the letter that matches each quotient to crack the code.

Letter Code

$4 \div 2 =$ **2** T $40 \div 5 =$ **8** N

$9 \div 3 =$ **3** K $35 \div 5 =$ **7** E

$7 \div 7 =$ **1** M $16 \div 4 =$ **4** R

$16 \div 2 =$ **8** S $25 \div 5 =$ **5** A

$18 \div 3 =$ **6** O $20 \div 2 =$ **10** W

What is another word for **cooperation?**

T E A M W O R K
2 7 5 1 10 8 4 3

HINT Think of dividing as sharing objects into equal groups.

56

Fill In the Blanks

Riley and Bing Bong divide and share their musical instruments. Twelve instruments divided between two people equals six instruments: $12 \div 2 = 6$.

Determine the missing numbers for each division sentence.

$42 \div 6 =$ **7** $16 \div 4 =$ **4**

10 $\div 2 = 5$ **30** $\div 5 = 6$

$35 \div$ **5** $= 7$ $24 \div$ **3** $= 8$

$21 \div 7 =$ **3** $10 \div 10 =$ **1**

24 $\div 3 = 8$ **12** $\div 6 = 2$

$18 \div$ **2** $= 9$ $49 \div$ **7** $= 7$

HINT Use your multiplication facts to help you figure out the missing number. For example, $2 \times 5 = 10$ helps solve ___ $\div 2 = 5$.

57

---

*Sample answers provided.

Answers

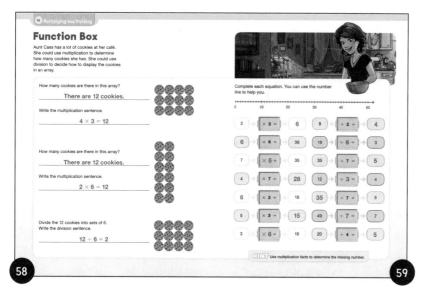

Function Box

Aunt Cass has a lot of cookies at her café. She could use multiplication to determine how many cookies she has. She could use division to decide how to display the cookies in an array.

How many cookies are there in this array?
There are 12 cookies.

Write the multiplication sentence.
4 × 3 = 12

How many cookies are there in this array?
There are 12 cookies.

Write the multiplication sentence.
2 × 6 = 12

Divide the 12 cookies into sets of 6. Write the division sentence.
12 ÷ 6 = 2

Complete each equation. You can use the number line to help you.

2 → × 3 = → 6
8 → + 2 = → 4
6 → × 6 = → 36
18 → ÷ 6 = → 3
7 → × 5 = → 35
35 → ÷ 7 = → 5
4 → × 7 = → 28
12 → ÷ 3 = → 4
6 → × 3 = → 18
35 → ÷ 7 = → 5
5 → × 3 = → 15
49 → ÷ 7 = → 7
3 → × 6 = → 18
20 → ÷ 4 = → 5

HINT Use multiplication facts to determine the missing number.

58 **59**

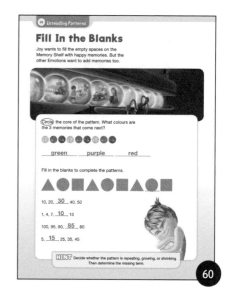

Fill In the Blanks

Joy wants to fill the empty spaces on the Memory Shelf with happy memories. But the other Emotions want to add memories too.

Circle the core of the pattern. What colours are the 3 memories that come next?

green   purple   red

Fill in the blanks to complete the patterns.

10, 20, **30**, 40, 50

1, 4, 7, **10**, 13

100, 95, 90, **85**, 80

5, **15**, 25, 35, 45

HINT Decide whether the pattern is repeating, growing, or shrinking. Then determine the missing term.

60

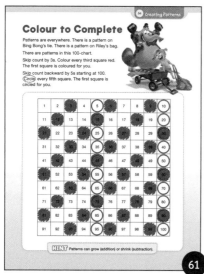

Colour to Complete

Patterns are everywhere. There is a pattern on Bing Bong's tie. There is a pattern on Riley's bag.

There are patterns in this 100-chart.

Skip count by 3s. Colour every third square red. The first square is coloured for you.

Skip count backward by 5s starting at 100. Circle every fifth square. The first square is circled for you.

HINT Patterns can grow (addition) or shrink (subtraction).

61

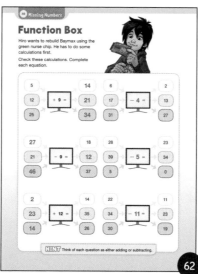

Function Box

Hiro wants to rebuild Baymax using the green nurse chip. He has to do some calculations first.

Check these calculations. Complete each equation.

12 + 9 = 21
25 → 34
17 − 4 = 13
31 → 27

21 − 9 = 12
46 → 37
39 − 5 = 34
5 → 0

23 + 12 = 35
14 → 26
34 − 11 = 23
30 → 19

HINT Think of each question as either adding or subtracting.

62

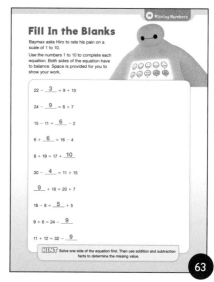

Fill In the Blanks

Baymax asks Hiro to rate his pain on a scale of 1 to 10.

Use the numbers 1 to 10 to complete each equation. Both sides of the equation have to balance. Space is provided for you to show your work.

22 − **3** = 9 + 10

24 − **9** = 8 + 7

15 − 11 = **6**

6 + **6** = 16 − 4

8 + 19 = 17 + **10**

30 − **4** = 11 + 15

9 + 18 = 20 + 7

18 − 8 = **5** + 5

9 + 6 = 24 − **9**

11 + 12 = 32 − **9**

HINT Solve one side of the equation first. Then use addition and subtraction facts to determine the missing value.

63

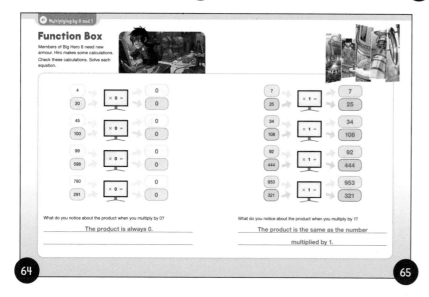

Function Box

Members of Big Hero 6 need new armour. Hiro makes some calculations. Check these calculations. Solve each equation.

4 → × 0 = → 0
20 → × 0 = → 0

7 → × 1 = → 7
25 → × 1 = → 25

45 → × 0 = → 0
100 → × 0 = → 0

34 → × 1 = → 34
108 → × 1 = → 108

99 → × 0 = → 0
598 → × 0 = → 0

92 → × 1 = → 92
444 → × 1 = → 444

780 → × 0 = → 0
291 → × 0 = → 0

953 → × 1 = → 953
321 → × 1 = → 321

What do you notice about the product when you multiply by 0?
The product is always 0.

What do you notice about the product when you multiply by 1?
The product is the same as the number multiplied by 1.

64 **65**

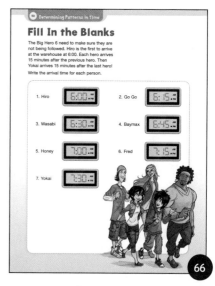

Fill In the Blanks

The Big Hero 6 need to make sure they are not being followed. Hiro is the first to arrive at the warehouse at 6:00. Each hero arrives 15 minutes after the previous hero. Then Yokai arrives 15 minutes after the last hero!

Write the arrival time for each person.

1. Hiro **6:00**
2. Go Go **6:15**
3. Wasabi **6:30**
4. Baymax **6:45**
5. Honey **7:00**
6. Fred **7:15**
7. Yokai **7:30**

66

106

*Sample answers provided.

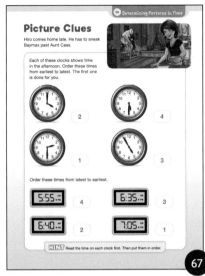

Picture Clues

Hiro comes home late. He has to sneak Baymax past Aunt Cass.

Each of these clocks shows time in the afternoon. Order these times from earliest to latest. The first one is done for you.

2   4

1   3

Order these times from latest to earliest.

5:55 — 4   6:35 — 3

6:40 — 2   7:05 — 1

HINT Read the time on each clock first. Then put them in order.

67

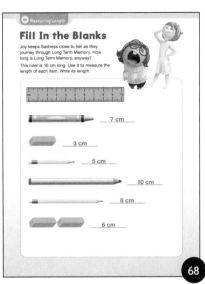

Fill In the Blanks

Joy keeps Sadness close to her as they journey through Long Term Memory. How long is Long Term Memory, anyway?
This ruler is 10 cm long. Use it to measure the length of each item. Write its length.

7 cm

3 cm

5 cm

10 cm

8 cm

6 cm

68

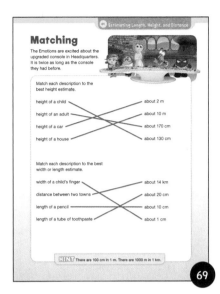

Matching

The Emotions are excited about the upgraded console in Headquarters. It is twice as long as the console they had before.

Match each description to the best height estimate.

height of a child   about 2 m
height of an adult   about 10 m
height of a car   about 170 cm
height of a house   about 130 cm

Match each description to the best width or length estimate.

width of a child's finger   about 14 km
distance between two towns   about 20 cm
length of a pencil   about 10 cm
length of a tube of toothpaste   about 1 cm

HINT There are 100 cm in 1 m. There are 1000 m in 1 km.

69

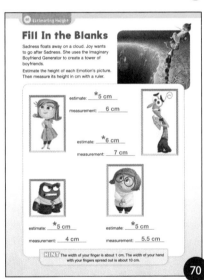

Fill In the Blanks

Sadness floats away on a cloud. Joy wants to go after Sadness. She uses the Imaginary Boyfriend Generator to create a tower of boyfriends.
Estimate the height of each Emotion's picture. Then measure its height in cm with a ruler.

estimate: *5 cm
measurement: 6 cm

estimate: *6 cm
measurement: 7 cm

estimate: *5 cm
measurement: 4 cm

estimate: *5 cm
measurement: 5.5 cm

HINT The width of your finger is about 1 cm. The width of your hand with your fingers spread out is about 10 cm.

70

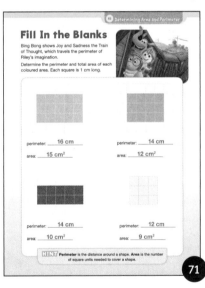

Fill In the Blanks

Bing Bong shows Joy and Sadness the Train of Thought, which travels the perimeter of Riley's imagination.
Determine the perimeter and total area of each coloured area. Each square is 1 cm long.

perimeter: 16 cm
area: 15 cm²

perimeter: 14 cm
area: 12 cm²

perimeter: 14 cm
area: 10 cm²

perimeter: 12 cm
area: 9 cm²

HINT Perimeter is the distance around a shape. Area is the number of square units needed to cover a shape.

71

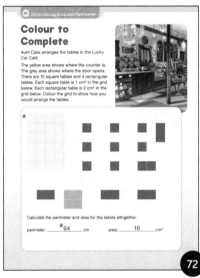

Colour to Complete

Aunt Cass arranges the tables in the Lucky Cat Café.

The yellow area shows where the counter is. The grey area shows where the door opens. There are 10 square tables and 4 rectangular tables. Each square table is 1 cm² in the grid below. Each rectangular table is 2 cm² in the grid below. Colour the grid to show how you would arrange the tables.

*

Calculate the perimeter and area for the tables altogether.

perimeter: *64 cm   area: 18 cm²

72

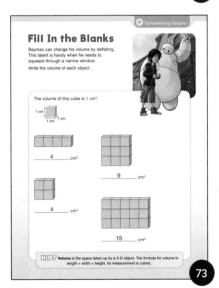

Fill In the Blanks

Baymax can change his volume by deflating. This talent is handy when he needs to squeeze through a narrow window.
Write the volume of each object.

The volume of this cube is 1 cm³.

1 cm
1 cm
1 cm

4 cm³

9 cm³

4 cm³

15 cm³

HINT Volume is the space taken up by a 3-D object. The formula for volume is length × width × height. Its measurement is cubed.

73

Picture Clues

Riley gets frustrated answering her parents' questions. A cold, sweet drink of lemonade could help her cool down.
Circle the container that would hold the greater amount of lemonade.

1.   2.

3.   4.

5.

74

Colour to Complete

Riley uses different containers to make different sounds. Containers with different capacities make different sounds.

Each of these beakers has a different capacity. Colour each beaker to show 250 mL.

Use red to colour the containers that hold more than 500 mL. Use yellow to colour the containers that hold less than 500 mL.

MILK

HINT To measure capacity, you can use millilitres (mL) or litres (L). There are 1000 millilitres in 1 litre.

75

*Sample answers provided.

Answers

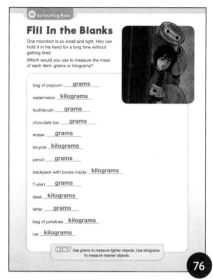

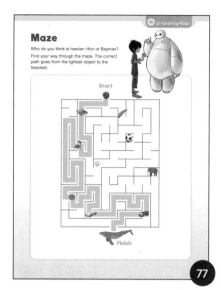

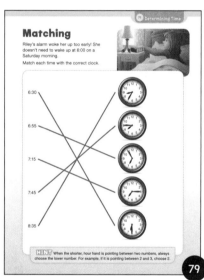

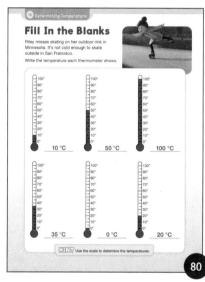

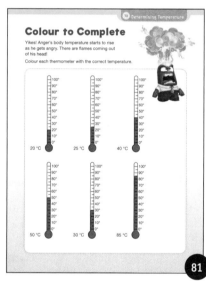

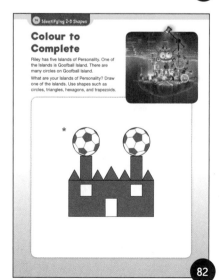

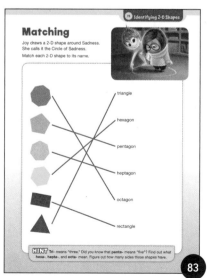

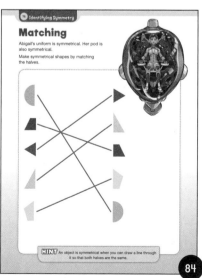

*Sample answers provided.

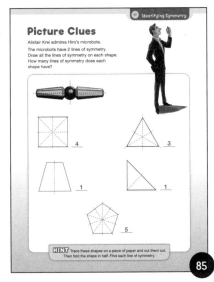

Picture Clues

Alistair Krei admires Hiro's microbots.
The microbots have 2 lines of symmetry.
Draw all the lines of symmetry on each shape.
How many lines of symmetry does each shape have?

4

3

1

1

5

HINT Trace these shapes on a piece of paper and cut them out. Then fold the shape in half. Find each line of symmetry.

85

Colour to Complete

Joy and Sadness watch as Friendship Island falls into the Memory Dump. As it falls, it rotates.
Colour each letter. Use the Colour Key.

Colour Key
rotated letters   reflected letters

HINT Reflecting means flipping an object across a line. Rotating means turning an object around.

86

Picture Clues

Riley is having a tough start to the day.
First she wakes up early. Then she squirts toothpaste onto her reflection in the mirror!
How is each image transformed? Choose either **reflected** or **rotated**. The first one is done for you.

reflected

reflected

rotated

rotated

reflected

87

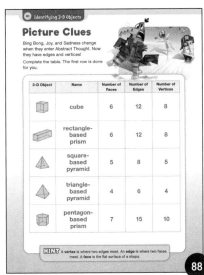

Picture Clues

Bing Bong, Joy, and Sadness change when they enter Abstract Thought. Now they have edges and vertices!
Complete the table. The first row is done for you.

3-D Object	Name	Number of Faces	Number of Edges	Number of Vertices
	cube	6	12	8
	rectangle-based prism	6	12	8
	square-based pyramid	5	8	5
	triangle-based pyramid	4	6	4
	pentagon-based prism	7	15	10

HINT A vertex is where two edges meet. An edge is where two faces meet. A face is the flat surface of a shape.

88

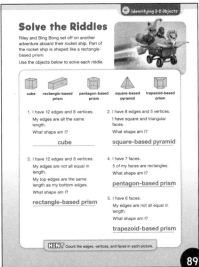

Solve the Riddles

Riley and Bing Bong set off on another adventure aboard their rocket ship. Part of the rocket ship is shaped like a rectangle-based prism.
Use the objects below to solve each riddle.

cube   rectangle-based prism   pentagon-based prism   square-based pyramid   trapezoid-based prism

1. I have 12 edges and 8 vertices.
My edges are all the same length.
What shape am I?
cube

2. I have 8 edges and 5 vertices.
I have square and triangular faces.
What shape am I?
square-based pyramid

3. I have 12 edges and 8 vertices.
My edges are not all equal in length.
My top edges are the same length as my bottom edges.
What shape am I?
rectangle-based prism

4. I have 7 faces.
5 of my faces are rectangles.
What shape am I?
pentagon-based prism

5. I have 6 faces.
My edges are not all equal in length.
What shape am I?
trapezoid-based prism

HINT Count the edges, vertices, and faces in each picture.

89

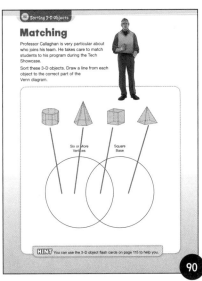

Matching

Professor Callaghan is very particular about who joins his team. He takes care to match students to his program during the Tech Showcase.
Sort these 3-D objects. Draw a line from each object to the correct part of the Venn diagram.

Six or More Vertices

Square Base

HINT You can use the 3-D object flash cards on page 115 to help you.

90

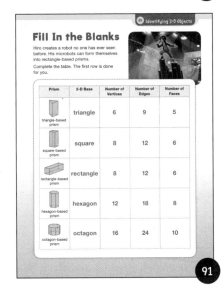

Fill In the Blanks

Hiro creates a robot no one has ever seen before. His microbots can form themselves into rectangle-based prisms.
Complete the table. The first row is done for you.

Prism	2-D Base	Number of Vertices	Number of Edges	Number of Faces
triangle-based prism	triangle	6	9	5
square-based prism	square	8	12	6
rectangle-based prism	rectangle	8	12	6
hexagon-based prism	hexagon	12	18	8
octagon-based prism	octagon	16	24	10

91

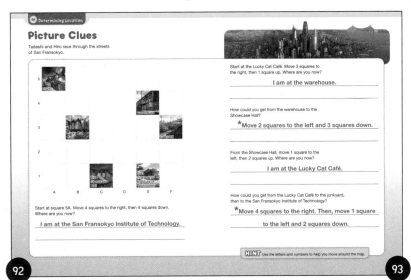

Picture Clues

Tadashi and Hiro race through the streets of San Fransokyo.

5

4

3

2

1

A   B   C   D   E   F

Start at square 5A. Move 4 squares to the right, then 4 squares down. Where are you now?

I am at the San Fransokyo Institute of Technology.

Start at the Lucky Cat Café. Move 3 squares to the right, then 1 square up. Where are you now?

I am at the warehouse.

How could you get from the warehouse to the Showcase Hall?

*Move 2 squares to the left and 3 squares down.

From the Showcase Hall, move 1 square to the left, then 2 squares up. Where are you now?

I am at the Lucky Cat Café.

How could you get from the Lucky Cat Café to the junkyard, then to the San Fransoyo Institute of Technology?

*Move 4 squares to the right. Then, move 1 square to the left and 2 squares down.

HINT Use the letters and numbers to help you move around the map.

92   93

*Sample answers provided.

Answers

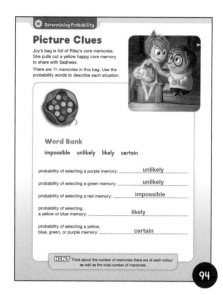

Picture Clues

Joy's bag is full of Riley's core memories. She pulls out a yellow happy core memory to share with Sadness.

There are 11 memories in this bag. Use the probability words to describe each situation.

Word Bank

impossible   unlikely   likely   certain

probability of selecting a purple memory: __unlikely__

probability of selecting a green memory: __unlikely__

probability of selecting a red memory: __impossible__

probability of selecting a yellow or blue memory: __likely__

probability of selecting a yellow, blue, green, or purple memory: __certain__

HINT Think about the number of memories there are of each colour as well as the total number of memories.

94

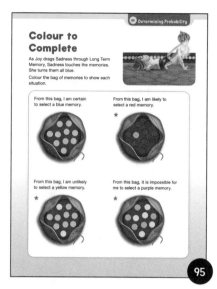

Colour to Complete

As Joy drags Sadness through Long Term Memory, Sadness touches the memories. She turns them all blue.

Colour the bag of memories to show each situation.

From this bag, I am certain to select a blue memory.

From this bag, I am likely to select a red memory. *

From this bag, I am unlikely to select a yellow memory. *

From this bag, it is impossible for me to select a purple memory.

95

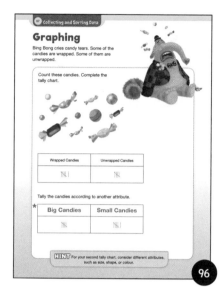

Graphing

Bing Bong cries candy tears. Some of the candies are wrapped. Some of them are unwrapped.

Count these candies. Complete the tally chart.

Wrapped Candies	Unwrapped Candies
₥₥ I	₥₥

Tally the candies according to another attribute.

Big Candies	Small Candies
₥₥	₥₥ I

*

HINT For your second tally chart, consider different attributes, such as size, shape, or colour.

96

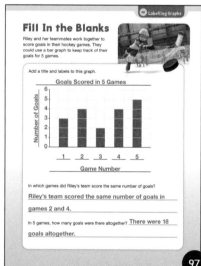

Fill In the Blanks

Riley and her teammates work together to score goals in their hockey games. They could use a bar graph to keep track of their goals for 5 games.

Add a title and labels to this graph.

Goals Scored in 5 Games

(bar graph: Number of Goals vs Game Number — 1:3, 2:4, 3:2, 4:4, 5:5)

In which games did Riley's team score the same number of goals?

Riley's team scored the same number of goals in games 2 and 4.

In 5 games, how many goals were there altogether? There were 18 goals altogether.

97

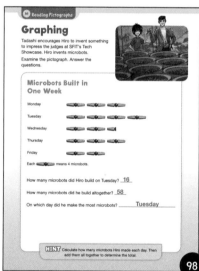

Graphing

Tadashi encourages Hiro to invent something to impress the judges at SFIT's Tech Showcase. Hiro invents microbots.

Examine the pictograph. Answer the questions.

Microbots Built in One Week

Monday

Tuesday

Wednesday

Thursday

Friday

Each means 4 microbots.

How many microbots did Hiro build on Tuesday? _16_

How many microbots did he build altogether? _58_

On which day did he make the most microbots? _Tuesday_

HINT Calculate how many microbots Hiro made each day. Then add them all together to determine the total.

98

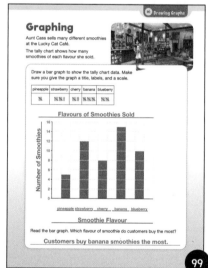

Graphing

Aunt Cass sells many different smoothies at the Lucky Cat Café.

The tally chart shows how many smoothies of each flavour she sold.

Draw a bar graph to show the tally chart data. Make sure you give the graph a title, labels, and a scale.

pineapple	strawberry	cherry	banana	blueberry
₥	₥₥ II	₥ III	₥₥ ₥₥	₥ ₥

Flavours of Smoothies Sold

(bar graph: Number of Smoothies vs Smoothie Flavour — pineapple:5, strawberry:12, cherry:8, banana:15, blueberry:10)

Read the bar graph. Which flavour of smoothie do customers buy the most?

Customers buy banana smoothies the most.

99

*Sample answers provided.

Learning Tools

1	2	3	4	5	6	7	8	9	10
11	12	13	14	15	16	17	18	19	20
21	22	23	24	25	26	27	28	29	30
31	32	33	34	35	36	37	38	39	40
41	42	43	44	45	46	47	48	49	50
51	52	53	54	55	56	57	58	59	60
61	62	63	64	65	66	67	68	69	70
71	72	73	74	75	76	77	78	79	80
81	82	83	84	85	86	87	88	89	90
91	92	93	94	95	96	97	98	99	100

×	1	2	3	4	5	6	7
1	1	2	3	4	5	6	7
2	2	4	6	8	10	12	14
3	3	6	9	12	15	18	21
4	4	8	12	16	20	24	28
5	5	10	15	20	25	30	35
6	6	12	18	24	30	36	42
7	7	14	21	28	35	42	49

Number	Hundreds	Tens	Ones

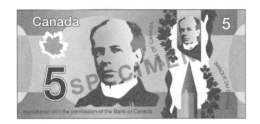

113

Cut out these flash cards. You can use them to learn more about 3-D objects.

Name: square-based
pyramid

Vertices: 5

Edges: 8

Faces: 5

Name: triangle-based
prism

Vertices: 6

Edges: 9

Faces: 5

Name: triangle-based
pyramid

Vertices: 4

Edges: 6

Faces: 4

Name: rectangle-based
prism

Vertices: 8

Edges: 12

Faces: 6

Name: rectangle-based
pyramid

Vertices: 5

Edges: 8

Faces: 5

Name: cube

Vertices: 8

Edges: 12

Faces: 6

Name: hexagon-based
prism

Vertices: 12

Edges: 18

Faces: 8

Name: hexagon-based
pyramid

Vertices: 7

Edges: 12

Faces: 7

Name: pentagon-based
prism

Vertices: 12

Edges: 18

Faces: 7

Cut out these flash cards. You can use them to learn more about 3-D objects.

Congratulations

_____!

Print your name.

You have finished the
Brain Boost learning path.
Way to go!